HOW TO GET THE MOST OUT OF YOUR POCKET CALCULATOR

HOW TO GET THE MOST OUT OF YOUR POCKET CALCULATOR

Henry Mullish

COLLIER BOOKS
A Division of Macmillan Publishing Co., Inc.
New York

COLLIER MACMILLAN PUBLISHERS
London

This book is dedicated to the memory of my kid brother Bubbles.

Macmillan Publishing Co., Inc.
866 Third Avenue, New York, N.Y. 10022
Collier-Macmillan Canada Ltd.

Library of Congress Catalog Card Number: 73-14112

FIRST COLLIER BOOKS EDITION 1973
SECOND PRINTING 1974

How to Get the Most Out of Your Pocket Calculator is published in a hardcover edition by Macmillan Publishing Co., Inc.

Printed in the United States of America

CONTENTS

2

3

4

ACKNOWLEDGMENTS

I would like to express my thanks to Dr. Melvin Hausner and Dr. Frances Bauer, who so kindly took the trouble to read the manuscript and offer criticism and helpful suggestions. I would also like to express my warm appreciation to Jimmy Lewis of the Computer Science Department of New York University, who is responsible not only for the Lewis method of finding the square root of a number—which is described in the book—but also for the section on Advanced Techniques (Appendix B), most of which is of his own design. Last, but by no means least, I am taking this opportunity to thank Stephen Kochan of S.U.N.Y. at Buffalo, who helped so much in improving the text, checking answers and examining the galley proofs with me.

INTRODUCTION

More than a hundred years ago the poet Wordsworth said, "The world is too much with us." He spoke for his own time, not foreseeing the immeasurably faster-moving, sometimes zany world we now inhabit. It has become necessary for many of us to develop into virtual wizards at accounting, bookkeeping, cost estimation and general clerical activities—merely to keep our economic heads above water.

But few of us have had the necessary training to handle the intricacies of business finance—or even household finance. Today even a routine trip to the supermarket often poses a severe drain on our mental resources. Thoughts like: "What is the most economical brand to buy?" and "Have I exceeded my budget?" are important concerns to bear in mind, particularly *before* one reaches the checkout counter.

As a direct spin-off of Space Age technology, we now have an exquisite tool to help us with these laborious everyday calculations. That tool is the *pocket calculator*—small, compact, lightweight, convenient, portable, battery-operated and extremely inexpensive to use.

Pocket calculators are rapidly becoming indispensable for the businessman, housewife and student alike. If the cost of the calculator continues to fall as it has since 1971, when they were first introduced to the general public, soon virtually every household will have one.

Students at the Harvard Graduate School of Business Administration currently rent such calculators for use in their classrooms. Engineers are scrapping their slide rules in favor of the more accurate pocket calculator. An expert educator who specializes in calculations has offered the view that schools will eventually have to alter their approach to the teaching of mathematics in order to allow for this new technology. He predicts that one day every student will have a calculator built into his desk, thus enabling teachers of mathematics to concentrate more on concepts and less on computation.

It has been estimated that in the year 1972 one million pocket calculators were sold—and that number is expected to double in 1973. Most of the calculators available are priced at around $100 but there are some others—no less compact, lightweight and portable—that sell at $50.

This calculator revolution is of very recent vintage. It was 1971 when a leading American electronics firm began to mass-produce the so-called one-chip calculator circuit. The chip is a very interesting development. Concentrated on a single piece of silicon, the size of a pin head, is a mass of electronic circuitry equivalent to 5,000 or even 6,000 transistors. The way this process of producing chips is carried out is complex; it uses a technology usually referred to as MOS/LSI, which stands for "metal oxide semiconductor/large scale integration." Advanced methods of mass-producing these chips were soon developed, resulting in a drastic cut in prices. This reduction in cost was helped along in part by the fact that much of the work involved was automated. Labor costs became minimal and American manufacturers could compete successfully with their traditional foreign competitors in countries where labor costs are much lower than those in the United States.

The pocket calculator is not, despite its appearance, a

toy or just an interesting novelty. It's a serious tool that can be indispensable to the person with the need to calculate problems of one kind or another. Its compactness and attractiveness can easily mislead one into thinking that the calculator is merely a plaything for the person who has everything else; it is not. As with all tools, it is of no use whatever until it is put to work. The automobile that remains sitting in the garage does no good (except perhaps to the ecology).

Like the automobile, the pocket calculator comes with a great variety of different features to suit most budgets and tastes. Some calculators will be preferred to others for different reasons. Some are turned on by the flick of a switch, some by opening a lid. Some are battery-operated only, others use either batteries or regular AC current. Some have rechargeable batteries enabling the user to operate the calculator for as long as 4–10 hours before plugging it into a wall socket to recharge the battery. Some operate only on standard American electrical current while others provide an option for either American or European current. Some have only a six-digit display panel while others have eight or even ten. Some have a "constant" feature, some not. Some are "fixed decimal" only while others are "floating decimal," permitting greater accuracy and ease of calculation.

It is because there are so many different kinds of calculators on the market today that we shall limit ourselves to describing three different kinds of *pocket calculators*—the lower-priced, medium-priced and higher-priced. We shall explain how to use each type efficiently, without being overly technical. We shall discuss a wide range of everyday problems, indicating not only a method to solve each problem but also how to solve the problem with the variously priced calculators.

HOW TO GET THE MOST OUT OF YOUR POCKET CALCULATOR

1

THE BASIC CALCULATOR (A)

1 | BECOMING FAMILIAR WITH THE LOWER-PRICED POCKET CALCULATOR

The price of the pocket calculator has come down so that it is within the reach of almost every household. How can we get the most out of it?

The uses to which the pocket calculator may be put are virtually limitless. This book will describe some typical problems, necessarily only a small fraction of those that may be solved quickly and efficiently by the pocket calculator.

A visit to the local department store or electronics dealer reveals the wide variety of pocket calculators available. They vary in cost from about $50 to $400, and they differ not only in price but in the numbers of keys they have, the different batteries they need, the kind of arithmetic operations they perform, the kinds of accessories they have and the optional features that are available.

They all have one thing in common, however: they all multiply, divide, add and subtract with pretty much the same speed and facility. How do they do it? The answer is Space Age technology. Today because we can concentrate the equivalent of as many as 5,000 transistors on a single silicon "chip" the size of a pin head (the very heart of each pocket calculator) the calculator can perform its mathematical wizardry at lightning speed.

When we look at the different kinds of pocket calculators, we notice that, on some, each arithmetic operation has its own key. The button for multiplication is marked with the "times" sign [×] and that for division is marked with the sign [÷] etc. On some calculators the key for addition, or sometimes the key for subtraction, is to be found on one button together with the "equals" sign. It might look like [=+] or [−=]. In order to understand the different kinds of keyboards that are available we shall first examine in detail a typical keyboard of one of the inexpensive models, one costing about $50.

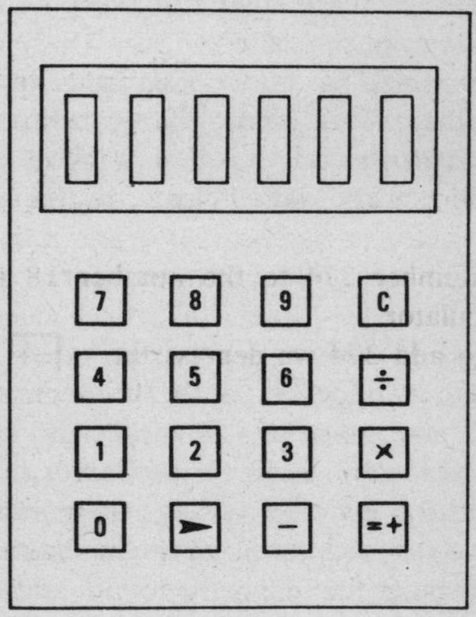

Keyboard of Lower-Priced Calculator

We notice that it has a display of six digits, below which are the keys for the numerals 0 through 9, and buttons marked [C] [÷] [×] [=+] [−] and a curious button, marked [►]. This is the "flip switch," about which we will have more to say later on.

For our first problem let us add the following two numbers:

Example 1 $18 + 374$

Of course most of us can add these two numbers in our heads without even pencil and paper, let alone an electronic calculating machine. But we want to understand exactly how such operations are performed on a pocket calculator.

First we switch the calculator to the "on" position. A zero appears in the right digit of the display.

Next we want to enter the number 18. We depress the 1 of the number 18 and we notice immediately that this 1 now replaces the zero that was previously displayed. Then the 8 is depressed. The 1 now shifts automatically left one position and the 8 appears on the extreme right. We have entered the number 18. What is needed now is to add the number 374 to the number 18 that is keyed into the calculator.

In order to add 374 we depress the [=+] button, but no change will be seen. To enter the second number we depress the 3 and notice that now the original number 18 disappears and the 3 is at the right. Depressing the 7 shifts the 3 over, and when the 4 is keyed in, *both* the digits 3 and 7 move left one place, leaving the number 374 displayed. Now both the numbers to be added have been entered into the calculator and all that remains to do is to depress the [=+] button and the answer, 392, is immediately displayed.

Let us now solve the following problem:

Example 2 49 + 3 + 128

If the calculator is still switched on we must first clear the display. Easy—depress the button marked C. The zero that again appears confirms that the display has been cleared. We now key in 49, depress the [=+] button, key in 3, again depress the [=+] button and key in 128. Depressing the [=+] button this time will give us our answer, 180.

We can indicate this simple series of steps in the following illustration, where each step is numbered consecutively and the operation performed and the display shown for each step is indicated.

Sequence	**1**	**2**	**3**	**4**	**5**	**6**	**7**
Operation	[C]	49	[=+]	3	[=+]	128	[=+]
Display	0	49	49	3	52	128	180

Let us now try a multiplication. For our first example let us multiply

Example 3 25 × 36

Sequence	**1**	**2**	**3**	**4**	**5**
Operation	[C]	25	[×]	36	[=+]
Display	0	25	25	36	900

Suppose now we want to multiply together two rather large numbers, say 123,456 and 654,321.

Example 4 123456 × 654321

Sequence	1	2	3	4	5
Operation	[C]	123456	[×]	654321	[=+]
Display	0	123456	123456	654321	807798

It would seem that the answer is 807,798, even though we feel sure that the correct answer is much bigger. The fact of the matter is that the six-digit display cannot hold any more digits. And this is where the "flip switch" is so useful. By depressing and holding the key marked [►] the remaining digits are revealed; they are 53376.

In other words, the correct result is

80,779,853,376

Not bad for such a small calculator, don't you think?

Now let us multiply together three numbers such that the result of the multiplication of the first two numbers exceeds the six-digit capacity of the display panel.

Example 5 1234 × 4321 × 2

Sequence	1	2	3	4	5
Operation	[C]	1234	[×]	4321	[×]
Display	0	1234	1234	4321	533211

Sequence	6	7	8	9
Operation	[►]	2	[=+]	[►]
Display	4	2	106642	2

What the scheme above suggests is that multiplying two numbers whose result (product) is greater than six digits will give the balance of the result in the display when the "flip switch" is depressed. This is certainly the case. But when the result is multiplied by 2, or any other number for that matter, it is only the first six digits which are multiplied, not the complete seven-digit product. In the case described above, the product 1234×4321 gives a product of 5,332,114. Obviously, when this number is multiplied by 2 one would expect a result of

10,664,228

and not

1,066,422

as obtained. One must be aware of this pitfall, that's all.

Let us leave multiplication for the present and move on to division. Here is our example:

Example 6 $456 \div 3$

Sequence	1	2	3	4	5
Operation	[C]	456	[÷]	3	[=+]
Display	0	456	456	3	152

While on the subject of division, let us now try to calculate

Example 7 $3 \div 456$

This will obviously give a very different result from that obtained in the previous division. Let us try it and see what happens.

Sequence	1	2	3	4	5
Operation	[C]	3	[÷]	456	[=+]
Display	0	3	3	456	0

According to the scheme shown above, the answer given is zero. Yet we know that although the result is certainly less than one, it is definitely not zero. In fact, it is between zero and one. Again, this is where the flip switch comes in handy. You will remember that this switch is the button marked [►]. When it is depressed the display shows what amounts to another six digits. In fact it now displays 006578. This should be read as

.006578

which is the correct answer. Releasing the flip switch will once again display the zero which really precedes the decimal point. Perhaps we should try another division of this kind.

Example 8 $175 \div 43$

Sequence	1	2	3	4	5	6
Operation	[C]	175	[÷]	43	[=+]	[►]
Display	0	175	175	43	4	069767

Thus the correct answer is

4.069767

The only remaining operation is subtraction. Let us once again take a very simple, but nevertheless practical, example. Suppose we want to compute

Example 9 $36 - 7$

First we enter 36. This is what one would expect. But next we depress the [=+] button. Then we enter 7, followed immediately by the minus sign. Here in our schematic form is what takes place:

Sequence	**1**	**2**	**3**	**4**	**5**
Operation	[C]	36	[=+]	7	[−]
Display	0	36	36	7	29

Thus the correct result of

29

is seen in the display. This seems an awkward way to subtract one number from another, but in the cheaper models that we are now describing this was the most inexpensive way to design the circuitry. When we explain the details of the medium-priced models we will show that this awkwardness does not exist. (For those inexpensive models where the minus sign shares the same button as the equal sign the procedure to follow is exactly the same as that above.)

But you may well ask, why not simply key in the following sequence, even in the inexpensive models:

Sequence	**1**	**2**	**3**	**4**	**5**
Operation	[C]	36	[−]	7	[=+]
Display	0	36	−36	7	−29

As can be seen, the result given is -29 rather than

29

the latter of which is the correct result.

Let us now try a slightly more involved problem.

Example 10 $17 \times 103 \times 14$

Sequence	**1**	**2**	**3**	**4**	**5**
Operation	[C]	17	[×]	103	[×]
Display	0	17	17	103	1751

Sequence	**6**	**7**
Operation	14	[=+]
Display	14	24514

Notice that after having calculated 17 times 103 it was *not* necessary to write down this intermediate answer and enter it again. It was retained in the "memory" of the calculator. Multiplying this intermediate result by 14 was straightforward and could be accomplished in the ordinary way. This is an example of a *chain calculation,* so called because it was not necessary to clear the calculator after the first multiplication. Each subsequent calculation could be done using the result previously obtained. In this way it resembles a chain of calculations, each calculation being a "link" in the chain.

What's more, we do not have to confine ourselves to

the same operation (multiplication) as in the previous example. Suppose we wanted to compute

Example 11 $36 \times 12 \div 4 + 10$

Sequence	1	2	3	4	5
Operation	[C]	36	[×]	12	[÷]
Display	0	36	36	12	432
Sequence	**6**	**7**	**8**	**9**	
Operation	4	[=+]	10	[=+]	
Display	4	108	10	118	

Here we have an example of a calculation that has a mixed sequence of instructions and again it was not necessary to re-enter any figures. This is called a *mixed calculation*. Thus we see that in both chain and mixed operations the intermediate result is retained by the calculator.

It is time now to talk dollars and cents. It is necessary to know how to work with numbers that have a decimal point, numbers like 50.25 that could be regarded as $50.25, and even numbers like 100.365 and .00125, etc. This despite the fact that we are presently discussing a pocket calculator that doesn't have provision for a decimal point. For our first example of such a calculation let us add together

Example 12 $196.37 + 45.68$

These numbers could represent two quantities of money, in dollars and cents. Since there is no provision for the decimal point we are now forced to remember that the decimal point is located between the 6 and the 3 in the first number and between the 5 and the 6 in the second number. Let us enter the numbers without the decimal point.

Sequence	**1**	**2**	**3**	**4**	**5**
Operation	[C]	19637	[=+]	4568	[=+]
Display	0	19637	19637	4568	24205

The result obtained, namely 24205, must be read *as if* the decimal point were between the 2 and the 0. The correct answer, therefore, is

242.05

It will be noticed that there were two "decimal places" in both the numbers added together and therefore there must be two decimal places in the result.

Let us now try to add together

Example 13 14.15 + 149.99 + 1542.36

Sequence	**1**	**2**	**3**	**4**	**5**
Operation	[C]	1415	[=+]	14999	[=+]
Display	0	1415	1415	14999	16414
Sequence		**6**	**7**		
Operation		154236	[=+]		
Display		154236	170650		

This time the result is

1706.50

again with two decimal places. Remember, with this type of calculator, the so-called "fixed point" calculator, it is up to the user to insert the decimal point in the correct place of the result.

2 | SQUARING A NUMBER

Whenever we multiply a number by itself we *square* it. For example, 10×10 is 10^2, read as "10 squared" or "10 raised to the power 2." We all know that the answer is 100. Even if we didn't know the result of 10×10, we could simply key 10 into the calculator and multiply it by 10, in the manner that has already been shown:

Example 14 10×10

Sequence	1	2	3	4	5
Operation	[C]	10	[×]	10	[=+]
Display	0	10	10	10	100

The result is clearly

100

Notice that it took five operations to accomplish this. A quicker way to do it is as follows:

Example 15 10^2

Sequence	1	2	3	4
Operation	[C]	10	[×]	[=+]
Display	0	10	10	100

where the correct result

100

is obtained in only four steps. By successively depressing the [×] and the [=+] buttons again we can compute 10^4. Let us, in fact, try our hand at raising the number 7 to the fourth power.

Example 16 7^4

Sequence	1	2	3	4	5	6
Operation	[C]	7	[×]	[=+]	[×]	[=+]
Display	0	7	7	49	49	2401

The final answer displayed

2401

is the correct result. What do you think would have been the result of depressing the [×] and [=+] keys again? You are right—it is the result of raising the number 7 to the eighth power:

$$7^8 = 5{,}764{,}801$$

where the digit 1, all the way over to the right (the least significant digit) is displayed by depressing the flip switch.

3 | CALCULATIONS INVOLVING DECIMAL FRACTIONS

On the inexpensive models there is no decimal key but, as we have already seen, this is not to say that calculations with numbers that contain decimal points cannot be performed on them. Two of our previous examples used numbers with decimals; but in both cases each value contained the *same number* of digits to the right of the decimal point. Is it possible to work with numbers when the number of digits to the right of the decimal point is different?

The answer is "yes"—provided that some elementary rules are obeyed. In order to understand what these rules are, we shall first discuss addition and subtraction, then multiplication, and finally division.

A | Keeping Track of the Decimal Point in Addition and Subtraction

In all cases where numbers are to be added or subtracted, make sure that each number has the same number of decimal places. If one has fewer than the others, simply add zeros to make it equal.

A simple example will illustrate this:

Example 17 $1.46 + 12 - 7.5$

This problem is equivalent to

$$1.46 + 12.00 - 7.50$$

and so we enter:

Sequence	1	2	3	4	5	6	7
Operation	[C]	146	[=+]	1200	[=+]	750	[−]
Display	0	146	146	1200	1346	750	596

This gives us the result 596. We now have to insert the decimal point in the answer so that it has two decimal places.

The correct answer is therefore

5.96

B | The Decimal Point in Multiplication

The rules for multiplying decimal numbers are easier than those for division, which we will discuss shortly. In multiplication, simply ignore the decimal points in each number. When the result is calculated, insert the decimal point so that it allows for as many places as the total number of decimal places in the entries.

Again, a simple example will clarify the matter:

Example 18 5.2×3.196

Sequence	1	2	3	4	5
Operation	[C]	52	[×]	3196	[=+]
Display	0	52	52	3196	166192

The result displayed is 166192. According to the rules for multiplication, we must insert the decimal point into this number at a specific location. To determine that location, we add the total number of decimal places in the two numbers being multiplied. The first has 1 place and the second 3 places, making a total of 4 decimal places. The true result therefore is

16.6192

C | The Decimal Point in Division

In order to divide two decimal numbers, make sure they both have the same number of decimal places by adding zeros, if necessary, to the one with the fewer decimal places.

A simple illustrative example:

Example 19 1475 ÷ 3.6

Sequence	1	2	3	4	5	6
Operation	C	14750	÷	36	=+	►
Display	0	14750	14750	36	409	722222

The integer portion of the number is given in the regular display, namely 409, and the decimal part is given by depressing the flip switch—that is, 722222.

The correct answer is therefore

409.722222

Let us take a further example. We shall now divide 3.456 by 6.3.

Example 20 3.456 ÷ 6.3

Sequence	1	2	3	4	5	6
Operation	C	3456	÷	6300	=+	►
Display	0	3456	3456	6300	0	548571

The true answer is therefore

0.548571

Example 21 $89 \times 37 \div 19$

Sequence	1	2	3	4	5
Operation	[C]	89	[×]	37	[÷]
Display	0	89	89	37	3293

Sequence	6	7	8
Operation	19	[=+]	[▶]
Display	19	173	315789

The correct answer is:

173.315789

Example 22 $\dfrac{(345 + 678) \times 58}{36}$

Sequence	1	2	3	4	5	6
Operation	[C]	345	[=+]	678	[=+]	[×]
Display	0	345	345	678	1023	1023

Sequence	7	8	9	10	11
Operation	58	[÷]	36	[=+]	[▶]
Display	58	59334	36	1648	166666

The answer is therefore

1648.166666

2

THE MEDIUM-PRICED CALCULATOR (B)

1 | BECOMING FAMILIAR WITH THE MEDIUM-PRICED POCKET CALCULATOR

Going from the lower-priced pocket calculator to the medium-priced calculator we naturally expect all kinds of improvements. And indeed we find them. However, on some of the lower-priced models the displays are easier to read than those on the more expensive models; this can be an important consideration when contemplating the purchase of a new calculator.

Most pocket calculators use displays of so-called light-emitting diodes (LED for short). These are semiconductors that usually emit a bright red glow when the low voltage from the batteries is applied. Most people have no difficulty reading this kind of display. However, persons who are color blind (almost exclusively males, for genetic reasons) have difficulty in reading red LED displays. Such people should select a calculator with a different colored display. Green has been found to be nearly ideal and there are various manufacturers who provide such a display in their calculators. The lower-priced model described in Chapter 1 has a mercury matrix tube display. This emits a crystal clear, easy-to-read, blue-green color.

This same inexpensive model is extremely economical so far as battery life is concerned. After it had inadvertently been left on for 15 hours, the author's calculator was still working, albeit with a faintly glowing display. On the more recent lower-priced models—especially those with LED displays (which use more current)—a jack is provided that allows you to connect the calculator, by means of a special charger-adapter, to a regular outlet, thus preserving battery life. It follows also that the more compact a calculator is, the smaller its batteries and the shorter their life span.

The physical characteristics of a typical medium-priced calculator resemble those of the lower-priced machine. It has the buttons 0 through 9, a separate equal-sign key, but *separate* buttons for the four arithmetic operations—multiplication, division, addition and subtraction. This permits the more natural "algebraic logic" rather than forcing you into following the "arithmetic logic" of the cheaper models. In addition to the arithmetic-function buttons, there is a button for the decimal point, a "clear" button marked [C], and another button marked [CE] that stands for "clear entry." It has an additional feature, the "chain-constant" switch. The last two features will be discussed shortly.

The medium-priced model has an "on-off" switch and an adapter to permit plugging the calculator into a regular wall outlet. Leaving the calculator plugged in overnight will usually charge the batteries fully if they are of the rechargeable type.

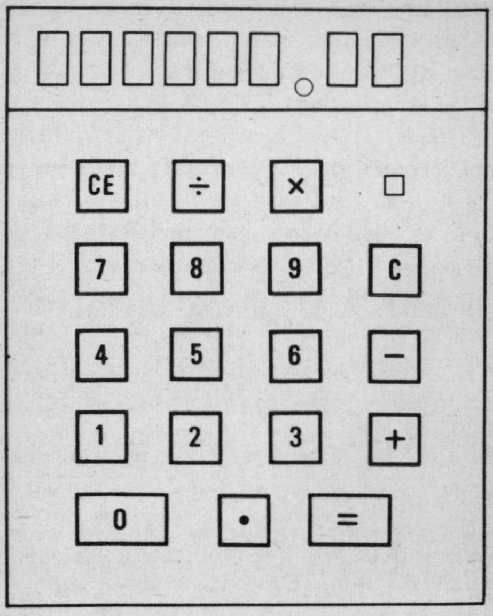

Keyboard of medium-price-range pocket calculator, selling for about $85

Switching the calculator on displays a zero followed by a decimal point at the extreme right of the display panel, which may hold eight digits. Move the "chain-constant" switch to "chain" and we are now ready to do our first example.

Example 23 12 + 35

Sequence	**1**	**2**	**3**	**4**	**5**
Operation	[C]	12	[+]	35	[=]
Display	0.	12.	12.	35.	47.

The answer is

47.

What is immediately apparent is that each time a number, for example 12, is keyed in, it appears on the display as 12. (the number followed by a decimal point). Since the circuitry of the chip is more sophisticated than on the less expensive models, the calculator permits what is called "full floating point decimal" operation. Thus you have a much more flexible machine at your disposal. It will accept whole numbers and/or numbers with decimal points and will calculate using such numbers *without the user's having to concern himself at all with the correct positioning of the decimal point in the result.* The calculator takes care of that and displays the true answer with the decimal point correctly positioned.

Let us use another simple example to illustrate this very important "point."

Example 24 1.234 + 5

Sequence	**1**	**2**	**3**	**4**	**5**
Operation	[C]	1.234	[+]	5	[=]
Display	0.	1.234	1.234	5.	6.234

The answer is displayed as

6.234

As described above, the calculator circuitry has placed the decimal point in its proper position.

Now let us examine the process of subtraction. In the previous chapter, subtracting a number on the lower-priced calculator was achieved by keying in that number and following it with the minus sign. On the more sophisticated medium-priced calculator one subtracts as one would do arithmetically. A simple example will illustrate this:

Example 25 $4 - 1$

Sequence	**1**	**2**	**3**	**4**	**5**
Operation	[C]	4	[−]	1	[=]
Display	0.	4.	4.	−1.	3.

Note that the answer displayed is

3.

even though we did not key in a decimal point.

Here are some examples of multiplication and division:

Example 26 53.1×62.123

Sequence	**1**	**2**	**3**	**4**	**5**
Operation	[C]	53.1	[×]	62.123	[=]
Display	0.	53.1	53.1	62.123	3298.7313

The answer displayed is

3298.7313

Example 27 5.216 ÷ 8.135

Sequence	1	2	3	4	5
Operation	[C]	5.216	[÷]	8.135	[=]
Display	0.	5.216	5.216	8.135	0.64118

The result displayed is

0.64118

Example 28 16 ÷ 4.12

Sequence	1	2	3	4	5
Operation	[C]	16	[÷]	4.12	[=]
Display	0.	16.	16.	4.12	3.8834951

The result displayed is

3.8834951

Example 29 (5 × 6.9) ÷ 3

Sequence	1	2	3	4	5	6	7
Operation	[C]	5	[×]	6.9	[÷]	3	[=]
Display	0.	5.	5.	6.9	34.5	3.	11.5

The result displayed is

11.5

When in "chain" mode the calculator is automatically cleared every time a number key is depressed followed immediately by the [=] key. Therefore, it is not really necessary to depress the [C] key after completing each of the calculations shown in this section. However, there is certainly no harm in doing so.

Chain calculations and mixed calculations are possible on this type as well as on the inexpensive models.

An example will help make this clear:

Example 30 $$\frac{(9.6 + 3)}{5} - 4.9$$

Sequence	**1**	**2**	**3**	**4**	**5**
Operation	[C]	9.6	[+]	3	[÷]
Display	0.	9.6	9.6	3.	12.6

Sequence	**6**	**7**	**8**	**9**
Operation	5	[−]	4.9	[=]
Display	5.	2.52	−4.9	−2.38

This time the result is the negative quantity

−2.38

On some models, the minus sign may appear on the extreme left of the display panel.

The next example is intended to show that depressing the [=] and following it by a *number* rather than an *arithmetic function* automatically clears the calculator.

This feature can be demonstrated by two successive calculations:

Example 31 16.1 × 4.23

1.2 ÷ 3.4

Sequence	**1**	**2**	**3**	**4**	**5**
Operation	[C]	16.1	[×]	4.23	[=]
Display	0.	16.1	16.1	4.23	68.103
Sequence	**6**	**7**	**8**	**9**	
Operation	1.2	[÷]	3.4	[=]	
Display	1.2	1.2	3.4	0.3529411	

From the above sequence it will be seen that the two separate results

68.103 and 0.3529411

can be obtained without clearing the calculator because after the [=] key was depressed a number was keyed in and the display was automatically cleared.

Now we come to a feature that was not present at all on the inexpensive calculator—the *constant* key. The constant key is convenient when one has the need either to multiply or to divide a whole series of numbers by a constant number.* This increases the flexibility of the calculator considerably.

* There are some calculators where the constant feature affects multiplication and division only. However, some are now available which extend the constant feature to addition and subtraction—and even to percentage.

Suppose, for example, we wish to multiply each of the the numbers 15, 12, 23 and 71 by 5. We could certainly do this individually in the "chain" mode as before, but it is quicker if we take advantage of the constant feature. *First, we put the "chain-constant" switch to the constant position:*

Example 32 15 × 5 12 × 5 23 × 5 71 × 5

Sequence	**1**	**2**	**3**	**4**	**5**	**6**	**7**
Operation	[C]	15	[×]	5	[=]	12	[=]
Display	0.	15.	15.	5.	75.	12.	60.

Sequence				**8**	**9**	**10**	**11**
Operation				23	[=]	71	[=]
Display				23.	115.	71.	355.

The four results obtained are

75. 60. 115. 355.

When the "chain constant" switch is in the "constant" position, a number entered after the [×] or the [÷] button—and directly before the [=] button is depressed—is retained in the "memory" of the calculator as a constant multiplier or divisor. This constant is erased by a subsequent entry of another constant in the manner described above or by depressing the [C] key.

Let us work through another example using the constant feature; this time let us assume we have a series of four numbers each of which we want to divide by the same constant factor, say 4.3.

Once again we make sure the calculator is switched to the *constant position.*

Example 33

23.3 ÷ 4.3   123 ÷ 4.3   1 ÷ 4.3   .0012 ÷ 4.3

Sequence	**1**	**2**	**3**	**4**	**5**	**6**
Operation	[C]	23.3	[÷]	4.3	[=]	123
Display	0.	23.3	23.3	4.3	5.4186046	123.

Sequence	**7**	**8**	**9**	**10**	**11**
Operation	[=]	1	[=]	.0012	[=]
Display	28.604651	1.	0.2325581	.0012	0.000279

From the above it is quite clear that the four answers

5.4186046   28.604651   0.2325581   0.000279

can be computed with minimum effort on the part of the user, by taking advantage of the constant feature. Businessmen, among others, will find this feature to be of particular usefulness when calculating percentages or discounts.

It should be noted, however, that the constant feature on some calculators treats the *first* number of a multiplication as the constant multiplier, rather than the *second* number—as assumed in the examples above.

The remaining arithmetic operation that can be performed on the medium-priced calculator is that of *ex-*

ponentiation, or raising a number to a power. For example:

$$10^2 = 10 \times 10 = 100$$
$$4^3 = 4 \times 4 \times 4 = 64$$
$$2^6 = 2 \times 2 \times 2 \times 2 \times 2 \times 2 = 64$$

Using the constant calculation mode, exponentiation can be done quite simply. You enter the number in the normal way and then press the multiplication button. The equal key is then depressed the same number of times as the power, *less one.* This works on the principle discussed in Chapter 1 where the displayed answer is used as the last entry.

Example 34 $3^4 = 3 \times 3 \times 3 \times 3$

Sequence	1	2	3	4	5	6
Operation	[C]	3	[×]	[=]	[=]	[=]
Display	0.	3.	3.	9.	27.	81.

Here,

81

is the correct answer. Note that the [=] was depressed $4 - 1 = 3$ times.

Some calculators in the medium-price range have an interesting battery-preserving feature. In order to save battery power the light-emitting diode display (LED) turns off automatically approximately 15 seconds after the last keyboard entry. This provides for the possibility that the user might have to attend to a telephone call or some other interruption in the middle of a lengthy calculation. If the calculator is left on with each of the LED's glowing, power from the batteries will, of course, be wasted. Instead, all but the extreme right digit in the display are turned off automatically by a clever timing device built into the circuitry of the calculator.

The presence of the single glowing digit is a reminder to the user that the calculator is still switched on and that the entry or result of the previous calculation, which faded out of view after 15 seconds or so, can be instantly recalled simply by pressing a special button that restores the display. From this point on, the calculation can be continued to its termination in the ordinary way.

There is another feature on some calculators, called the *clear entry* key. Suppose, for example, that during a computation you inadvertently enter the wrong number. If this mistake is caught immediately, the number in error can be erased simply by pressing the [CE] key. You can then enter the correct number and continue the calculation without having to recommence the calculation from the beginning. In other words, although an incorrectly entered number has been erased and corrected, none of the previous calculation has been lost.

2 | FINDING THE SQUARE ROOT OF A NUMBER

The square root of a number n is that number which, when multiplied by itself, gives n. For example:

$$5 \times 5 = 25$$

Therefore the square root of 25 is 5. This is usually represented as:

$$\sqrt{25} = 5$$

By the same token,

$$\sqrt{100} = 10 \qquad \sqrt{144} = 12 \qquad \sqrt{400} = 20$$

$$\sqrt{2} = 1.4142135$$

How would one find the square root of a number using the medium-priced pocket calculator? There is no square-root function on these calculators although it is to be found on the more expensive models. However, with a little patience and ingenuity it is possible to find the exact square root of a number even on the medium-priced, floating-decimal pocket calculator. The technique used goes back into history. Devised by Sir Isaac Newton and later refined by Joseph Raphson, a contemporary of Newton, it is called the Newton-Raphson technique. It is the same technique that the giant computers use to compute the square root.

Let us examine the method. Assume that our task is to find the square root of 10. The method successively finds approximations to the square root, homing in on the answer after a series of repetitions.

The formula is as follows:

$$\text{approximate square root} = \frac{1}{2}\left(\frac{\text{number}}{\text{guess}} + \text{guess}\right)$$

This means that if our initial guess is 1 and the number whose square root is required is 10, our first result (approximation) will be given by:

$$\text{First approximation: } \frac{1}{2}\left(\frac{10}{1} + 1\right) = 5.5$$

This result of 5.5 is now "plugged in" to the formula as the new guess. Thus we compute the second approximation as follows:

$$\text{Second approximation: } \frac{1}{2}\left(\frac{10}{5.5} + 5.5\right) = 3.6590909$$

The number 3.6590909 is now used as the next guess. Here now is our third approximation:

Third approximation:

$$\frac{1}{2}\left(\frac{10}{3.6590909}+3.6590909\right)=3.196005$$

Continuing the process we get:

Fourth approximation: 3.1624556

Fifth approximation: 3.1622776

Sixth approximation: 3.1622776

This fifth result is, in fact, the best approximation to the true square root of 10 because no change is found on the sixth repetition. For larger numbers than 10 it is advisable to select as a first guess a number that is reasonably close to the approximate square root. This will make the task of finding the square root much quicker.

The problem we just did may be summarized in the usual way. The only difference this time is that we have to write down on a scratch pad the resulting approximation.

Example 35 $\sqrt{10} = ?$

Sequence	**1**	**2**	**3**	**4**	**5**
Operation	[C]	10	[÷]	1	[+]
Display	0.	10.	10.	1.	10.

Sequence	**6**	**7**	**8**	**9**
Operation	1	[÷]	2	[=]
Display	1.	11.	2.	5.5

The result of

5.5

is now substituted as the new guess. Therefore we go back to step 2, enter 10 again and divide by 5.5 (step 4) instead of 1 and add 5.5 instead of 1 (step 6).

This process is repeated, always using the last result as the new guess. The final result of

3.1622776

is the true square root of 10.

The square root of a number is instantly obtainable on the higher-priced calculator that we shall discuss later. However, we first present some exercises for the reader, plus a varied list of typical household problems that could indeed be most vexing to solve without a calculator.

In order to gain some confidence in your ability to handle the pocket calculator—whichever kind you may have—we suggest you try your hand at solving the following problems and compare the results you obtain with those shown in Appendix E. If you disagree with the printed result the chances are that you made an error. Simply recalculate the problem until your result agrees with the printed result—or at least until it very closely agrees. Not all calculators contain the same number of digits; the greater the number of digits in the display, the more accurate the result may be.

In the sample problems that follow, write out your answers *before* you look at the solutions given in Appendix E.

3 | SAMPLE PROBLEMS

All Calculators

(1) $596 + 42$

(2) $27.69 + 19.537$

(3) $1942 - 368$

(4) $9.4 - 3.6$

(5) 19×43

(6) 2.164×3.18

(7) $53 \div 7$

(8) $19.6 \div 14.19$

(9) $(4 \times 37.6) \div 6$

(10) $\dfrac{(9.4 + 3.2)}{5} - 6.9$

Calculators with Constant Feature

(11) Multiply all of the following numbers by 63.1, using the constant feature:

(a) 54
(b) 106.2
(c) .001
(d) −42.6
(e) 1234.56

(12) Divide all of the numbers in Exercise 11 by 1.23, using the constant feature.

(13) Calculate the following exponentials:

(a) 2^2
(b) 3^5
(c) 7^4
(d) 6^5
(e) $(7.13)^3$

(14) Using the Newton-Raphson technique, calculate the square roots of the following numbers:

(a) 35
(b) 50
(c) 120
(d) 1234

3

SOLVING SOME COMMON HOUSEHOLD PROBLEMS

1 | DETERMINING GASOLINE CONSUMPTION OF A CAR

There is much current talk about the "energy crisis" and we hear fears expressed about the possibility of having to ration gasoline. Whether this concern is real or not, the everyday automobile user has good reason to worry about how many miles he is getting to the gallon. Some careful motorists, incidentally, keep a continuous record of their gas consumption; not only does it provide a useful record of their expenses, but a sudden drop in gasoline efficiency serves as an indication of engine trouble. It is surprisingly easy to calculate gasoline consumption accurately, in the following way.

Fill up the gas tank and make a note of the reading on the odometer (the mileage gauge).

Drive until the tank is, say, half empty. Again fill up with gas and this time take careful note of how many gallons are required to fill the tank. Also take down the new reading on the odometer.

Let us assume the following:

First odometer reading	25,162 miles
Second odometer reading	25,321 miles
Number of gallons required to fill tank	9.2 gallons
Distance covered	25,321 − 25,162 = 159 miles

Therefore, 159 miles used 9.2 gallons of gasoline. The number of miles per gallon is found by calculating

$$\frac{159}{9.2}$$

Here is how the whole calculation is done swiftly and efficiently, using either the lower-priced (A) or the medium-priced (B) pocket calculator.

Example 36 Measuring Gasoline Consumption (A)

Sequence	1	2	3	4	5
Operation	[C]	25321	[=+]	25162	[−]
Display	0	25321	25321	25162	159

Sequence	6	7	8	9
Operation	[÷]	92	[=+]	[▶]
Display	159	92	1	728260

The answer would appear to be 1.728260, but in view of the fact that we divided by 92 rather than 9.2 we have to shift the decimal point one digit to the right.

The correct result is therefore

17.28260 miles per gallon

On the calculator with the floating decimal feature, the problem is slightly easier to solve. Here is the way to calculate gas consumption on the medium-priced calculator.

Example 37 Measuring Gasoline Consumption (B)

Sequence	1	2	3	4	5
Operation	[C]	25321	[−]	25162	[÷]
Display	0.	25321.	25321.	−25162.	159.

Sequence	6	7
Operation	9.2	[=]
Display	9.2	17.282608

2 | BALANCING THE CHECKBOOK

With a pocket calculator, it need no longer be drudgery to balance your checkbook when the bank sends its periodic statement.

Let us say that your checkbook balance reads $454.20. Look at the date of the statement and make two separate totals. The first is the sum of all the deposits made since the date of the statement. Say this is $423.00. The second is the sum of all the checks that are outstanding. Suppose this sum to be $210.16.

Procedure for Balancing Checking Account

Balance according to statement	$241.36
Sum of deposits made since statement date	423.00
Total	664.36
Checks outstanding	210.16
Total	454.20
Checkbook balance	$454.20

On the calculator it becomes trivial:

Example 38 *Balancing Checking Account* (A)

Sequence	1	2	3	4	5	6	7
Operation	[C]	24136	[=+]	42300	[=+]	21016	[−]
Display	0	24136	24136	42300	66436	21016	45420

Example 38 *Balancing Checking Account* (B)

Sequence	1	2	3	4	5
Operation	[C]	241.36	[+]	423.00	[−]
Display	0.	241.36	241.36	423.00	664.36

Sequence	6	7
Operation	210.16	[=]
Display	−210.16	454.2

Note the suppression of the zero in the result 454.2. A trailing zero should be added mentally.

In each case the checkbook total is balanced, with $454.20 corresponding to the computed value based on the statement balance, deposits and outstanding checks. Needless to say, the totals of deposits made since the statement and of checks outstanding can also be swiftly and accurately computed with the calculator.

3 | SHOPPING FOR THE "BEST BUY" IN THE STORE

The harried shopper is constantly being confronted with the task of having to decide which of a variety of sizes of the same item is most economical in terms of dollars and cents.

For example, assume a store is selling a certain kind of grape jelly in three different sizes as follows:

7-ounce can	63¢
12-ounce can	89¢
16-ounce can	$1.10

The method of deciding which size is the most economical is to calculate the unit price for each size. All this means is that one calculates the cost per unit quantity—in this case, per ounce. In other words, we have to calculate the following three quantities:

$$63 \div 7$$
$$89 \div 12$$
$$110 \div 16$$

The smallest of these results will represent the most economical buy.

With the lower-priced calculator, the steps are as follows:

Example 39 *The Most Economical Buy* (A)

Sequence	**1**	**2**	**3**	**4**	**5**
Operation	[C]	63	[÷]	7	[=+]
Display	0	63	63	7	9

Sequence	**1**	**2**	**3**	**4**	**5**
Operation	89	[÷]	12	[=+]	[▶]
Display	89	89	12	7	416666

Sequence	**1**	**2**	**3**	**4**	**5**
Operation	110	[÷]	16	[=+]	[▶]
Display	110	110	16	6	875000

From the above series of calculations it will be seen that the unit prices are respectively

9¢ 7.42¢ 6.88¢

per ounce, which makes the third size, the 16-ounce size, the most economical buy. This result is confirmed by the medium-priced pocket calculator, which calculates the unit prices in a similar fashion.

While on the subject of the supermarket it might be of interest to the reader to know that food merchandising is about to undergo a drastic change: plans are well under way to automate the checkout counter. Within the next two or three years we might not see any more manual-checkout employees as we know them today. Instead, a computer will scan the items for price and total up the bill for the customer. The checker will simply guide the purchased items across the optical scanner with one hand and immediately bag the items for the customer.

The automation of the checkout counter should enable the customer to get through in half the time it now takes to shop. And the decided savings in costs for the supermarket could be passed on to the customer as well.

Under such a system the individual package or can will not carry a price stamped on it as it does today. The price will be displayed only on the shelf. Without a pocket calculator, the purchaser will not easily be able to confirm the total amount charged at the automated checkout counter.

4

USE OF THE CALCULATOR IN ACCOUNTANCY

One of the major users of calculator equipment is the accountant, whether he is a private accountant, employee of an accounting firm or a corporate accountant. All accountants have been using calculators for many years, but the equipment tended to be large, bulky and relatively slow, before the advent of the pocket calculator.

1 | CALCULATING THE PERCENTAGE OF INCREASE AND DECREASE

Frequently an accountant has to analyze the increase of a specific item from one period to another. For example, he might want to compare sales, expenses, gross payrolls, or profit from one period to another.

Suppose, for example, in 1974 an automobile dealer sold 365 cars whereas in 1973 he sold 243 automobiles. Two meaningful questions now present themselves.

a. What was the increase (or decrease) of cars sold?
b. What was the percentage increase (or decrease) of cars sold?

The first question is merely the difference between 365 and 243:

$$365 - 243 = 122$$

In other words, there was an increase of 122 cars sold in 1974 over those sold in 1973.

The formula computing the percentage of increase (question b) is:

% Increase (or Decrease) =

$$\left(\frac{\text{current period} - \text{previous period}}{\text{previous period}}\right) \times 100$$

That is,

$$\left(\frac{365 - 243}{243}\right) \times 100$$

If the result of the subtraction is negative, it simply means that there is a decrease rather than an increase. Be sure, in calculating such problems, that the divisor (in our case 243) is *always* the previous period.

Example 40 Percentage Increase (or Decrease) (A)

Sequence	**1**	**2**	**3**	**4**	**5**	**6**
Operation	[C]	365	[=+]	243	[−]	[×]
Display	0	365	365	243	122	122

Sequence	**7**	**8**	**9**	**10**	**11**
Operation	100	[÷]	243	[=+]	[▶]
Display	100	12200	243	50	205761

The answer with the low-priced model is therefore

50.2%

where the rest of the fraction is ignored. Notice the order

in which this calculation is done. The expression above could have been written as

$$\frac{(365 - 243) \times 100}{243}$$

This form is preferred because, in general, division should be last.

On the medium-priced calculator, the same calculation would be done as follows:

(B)

Sequence	1	2	3	4	5
Operation	[C]	365	[−]	243	[÷]
Display	0.	365.	365.	−243.	122.

Sequence	6	7	8	9
Operation	243	[×]	100	[=]
Display	243.	0.5020576	100.	50.20576

Let us now look at a typical expense sheet of a fictitious company.

Expense Sheet

Description	1972	1973	Change + or −	% Change + or −
Typing	5,672.00	4,791.00	−881.00	−15.53
Travel	1,251.00	3,596.00	2,345.00	187.45
Payroll	111,491.00	122,592.00	11,101.00	9.96
Rent	11,585.00	10,496.00	−1,089.00	.....
Miscellaneous	3,242.00	4,311.00	1,069.00	.....

The last two percentages are not shown. They have been

left as an exercise for the reader to complete. The calculated results may be checked by comparing them with the answers shown in Appendix E.

2 | CALCULATING INVENTORY

Every company that keeps a stock of any kind of merchandise must periodically take an inventory to determine the actual value of merchandise in its possession. The frequency of taking inventory is influenced to a large extent by the kind of business conducted, and may be taken once a month or perhaps once or twice a year.

Let us concoct a simplified inventory for a clothing factory.

Inventory

Quantity	Description	Cost	Total
1090	Cards of buttons	.05 per card	54.50
500 yds	Fabric A	3.15 per yard	....
750 yds	Fabric B	4.00 per yard	....
25 yds	Fabric C	4.15 per yard	....
2000 reels	Cotton	0.10 per reel	....
4500	Needles	0.01 per needle	....
120 bars	Soap	0.15 per bar	....
			$4,996.25 Total

In calculating the total value of the inventory each line must be dealt with separately. Once again, (A) refers to the lower-priced calculator and (B) to the medium-priced.

Example 41 *Calculating Inventory* (A)

Sequence	**1**	**2**	**3**	**4**	**5**
Operation	[C]	1090	[×]	5	[=+]
Display	0	1090	1090	5	5450

Thus the value for the first item is

$54.50

Example 41 *Calculating Inventory* (B)

Sequence	**1**	**2**	**3**	**4**	**5**
Operation	[C]	1090	[×]	.05	[=]
Display	0.	1090.	1090.	.05	54.5

Calculate the numbers (products) that should be entered in the right-hand column and then total them. Your answer should be:

$4,996.25

If your answer is different, the error probably lies in the calculation of one of the items. You can check these individual totals in Appendix E.

3 | CALCULATING THE GRAND TOTAL OF SUMS

Every accountant has a need to find the grand total of sums for much of his work. It is merely the name given to an arrangement of figures that is composed of a series of columns. Each column is summed and then each of these totals is summed to provide the grand total. It is a straightforward exercise in adding. Let us try one.

14.62	7.01	3.22	
15.49	4.32	7.99	
123.45	2.34	8.00	
1.23	10.11	4.00	
9.68	11.28	1.29	
164.47	35.06	24.50	$224.03

Example 42 *Grand Total of Sums* (A).

Sequence	1	2	3	4	5	6
Operation	[C]	1462	[=+]	1549	[=+]	12345
Display	0	1462	1462	1549	3011	12345

Sequence	7	8	9	10	11
Operation	[=+]	123	[=+]	968	[=+]
Display	15356	123	15479	968	16447

And similarly for the other two columns; then take the grand total of the three columns.

Now try your hand at calculating the grand total of

sums of the following set of figures. You will find the answers to compare against your own in Appendix E.

17.31	149.62	59.33
48.91	22.55	28.12
102.00	17.31	12.28
7.33	8.61	13.99

4 | CALCULATING DISTRIBUTION OF EXPENSES

Let us assume that a company has a rental bill of $146,000 to pay. The company is composed of six departments and it is decided to apportion the cost of the rent among the departments based on the net sales of the previous year. Assume the individual department net sales for the previous year are as shown:

Appliances division	$320,400
Household division	122,512
Ladies wear	131,472
Mens wear	98,711
Cosmetics	18,495
Sporting goods	21,600
	$713,190

To calculate the factor for distribution of the rental expense, one divides the rent, $146,000, by the total net sales.

$$\frac{\text{rental}}{\text{net sales}} = \frac{146{,}000}{713{,}190} = 0.204714$$

This factor of 0.204714 is now multiplied by the net sales for each department. Here is what the schematic looks like for the lower-priced pocket calculator.

Example 43 *Distribution Factor* (A)

Sequence	1	2	3	4	5	6
Operation	[C]	146000	[÷]	713190	[+=]	[►]
Display	0	146000	146000	713190	0	204714

The result of

0.204714

is the factor for distribution.

Using the medium-priced calculator:

(B)

Sequence	1	2	3	4	5
Operation	[C]	146000	[÷]	713190	[=]
Display	0.	146000.	146000.	713190.	0.204714

We are now ready to multiply the net sales *for each department* by the distribution factor of 0.204714.

Since we have to key a series of numbers, the schematic for the low-priced calculator looks somewhat lengthy. Do not be fazed by this.

Example 44 *Calculating the Distributed Expense* (A)

Sequence	1	2	3	4	5	6
Operation	[C]	204714	[×]	320400	[=+]	[►]
Display	0	204714	204714	320400	655903	65600

Sequence	7	8	9	10	11	12
Operation	C	204714	×	122512	=+	►
Display	0	204714	204714	122512	250799	21568

Sequence	13	14	15	16	17	18
Operation	C	204714	×	131472	=+	►
Display	0	204714	204714	131472	269141	59008

Sequence	19	20	21	22	23	24
Operation	C	204714	×	98711	=+	►
Display	0	204714	204714	98711	202075	23654

Sequence	25	26	27	28	29	30
Operation	C	204714	×	18495	=+	►
Display	0	204714	204714	18495	378618	5430

Sequence	31	32	33	34	35	36
Operation	C	204714	×	21600	=+	►
Display	0	204714	204714	21600	442182	2400

It can now be seen that the distributed expenses, rounded out to the nearest dollar, are as follows:

Appliances division	$65,590
Household division	25,080
Ladies wear	26,914
Mens wear	20,208
Cosmetics	3,786
Sporting goods	4,422

Totaling these expenses we confirm that the sum agrees with the total rental expense of $146,000.

There is no question that such a detailed calculation requires many steps. Nevertheless, the inexpensive calculator can handle the problem quickly, accurately and fairly conveniently. The step that created the repetitive work was having to key into the calculator the value .204714 for each department.

On the medium-priced calculator with the constant switch this repetition is not needed, since this *same* factor needs to be entered *only once* and remains constant, to be multiplied each time by the net sales figure for each department.

With the *constant switch on,* here is what is entailed schematically:

(B)

Sequence	1	2	3	4
Operation	[C]	320400	[×]	.204714
Display	0.	320400.	320400.	0.204714

Sequence	5	6	7	8
Operation	[=]	122512	[=]	131472
Display	65590.365	122512.	25079.921	131472.

Sequence	9	10	11	12
Operation	[=]	98711	[=]	18495
Display	26914.159	98711.	20207.523	18495.

Sequence	13	14	15
Operation	[=]	21600	[=]
Display	3786.1854	21600.	4421.8224

We arrived at the same results using only 15 steps instead of the 36 steps required previously. This is an example of the major use of the constant option.

5 | PAYROLLS

If a firm has its own accountant the payroll will often be prepared by him. The rates at which people are paid vary widely. Some are paid on an hourly basis, whereas others may have overtime or piecework bonuses. What we shall describe here are a few of the most common problems related to payrolls.

A | Straight Hourly Payroll

Employees receiving only a straight hourly pay are not compensated for any overtime they may work. The calculation of their pay is, of course, very simple.

Let us assume an employee earns at the rate of $4.35 per hour. He works 40 hours in a particular week and receives his gross pay of 40 × 4.35 less deductions of various kinds. These deductions may include federal tax (32.15), social security (6.30), city tax (2.14) and state tax (3.52), which are usually arrived at by looking up the gross pay on a tax chart. On a lower-priced calculator the calculation would be:

Sequence	1	2	3	4	5	6	7
Operation	[C]	40	[×]	435	[=+]	3215	[−]
Display	0	40	40	435	17400	3215	14185

Sequence	8	9	10	11	12	13
Operation	630	[−]	214	[−]	352	[−]
Display	630	13555	214	13341	352	12989

Thus the net pay is $129.89. We arrive at the same figure using the medium-priced calculator.

(B)

Sequence	1	2	3	4	5
Operation	[C]	40	[×]	4.35	[−]
Display	0.	40.	40.	4.35	174.

Sequence	6	7	8	9
Operation	32.15	[−]	6.30	[−]
Display	−32.15	141.85	−6.30	135.55

Sequence	10	11	12	13
Operation	2.14	[−]	3.52	[=]
Display	−2.14	133.41	−3.52	129.89

As an exercise, assume the following data for a part-time employee working on an hourly system during one month:

53 hours @ $3.88 per hour	
Federal tax	63.90
Social security	10.00
City tax	5.10
State tax	8.50

Calculate the gross pay and net pay. (Correct answers are in Appendix E.)

B | Overtime Payroll

The overtime payroll implies that a premium rate is paid for hours worked beyond a fixed amount, say 35 hours per week.

A typical employee's paycheck may be made up as follows:

35 hours @ $3.80 per hour
7 hours @ 1½ time, or $5.70 per hour

This would represent his gross pay. From it would be deducted his various taxes, for example:

Federal tax	28.68
Social security	5.98
City tax	4.62
State tax	5.18

As usual, we begin with the low-priced calculator. After step 5 of the calculation you will need to write down the result (133.00) for use later on in step 11.

(A)

Sequence	1	2	3	4	5
Operation	[C]	35	[×]	380	[=+]
Display	0	35	35	380	13300

Sequence	6	7	8	9	10
Operation	[C]	7	[×]	570	[=+]
Display	0	7	7	570	3990

Sequence	11	12	13	14	15
Operation	13300	[=+]	2868	[−]	598
Display	13300	17290	2868	14422	598

Sequence	16	17	18	19	20
Operation	[−]	462	[−]	518	[−]
Display	13824	462	13362	518	12844

The net pay is thus seen to be $128.44, a figure that is also obtained in similar fashion using the medium-priced calculator. Again, 133. is written down after step 5.

(B)

Sequence	1	2	3	4	5
Operation	[C]	35	[×]	3.80	[=]
Display	0.	35.	35.	3.80	133.

[133. is written down]

Sequence	6	7	8	9	10
Operation	[C]	7	[×]	5.70	[+]
Display	0.	7.	7.	5.70	39.9

Sequence	11	12	13	14	15
Operation	133.	[−]	28.68	[−]	5.98
Display	133.	172.9	−28.68	144.22	−5.98

Sequence	16	17	18	19	20
Operation	[−]	4.62	[−]	5.18	[=]
Display	138.24	−4.62	133.62	−5.18	128.44

The overtime payroll illustrated in the last example involves the writing of certain intermediate results. The reader might enjoy finding a way to eliminate this unnecessary operation. As a sample exercise, let us assume the following data for an employee working on overtime:

35 hours @ $4.20 per hour
12 hours @ 1½ time

His deductions are:

Federal tax	48.85
Social security	10.85
City tax	7.25
State tax	8.68

Calculate the gross and net pay, then check your answers with Appendix E.

C | Piecework Payroll

Some manufacturers pay their employees according to

the number of items produced with no minimum or guaranteed pay. Thus, a garment maker might be compensated on a piecework basis, with different rates for different items according to the following list:

		Number Produced
Shirts	@ 1.80 each	12
Blouses	@ 1.15 each	32
Skirts	@ 1.25 each	39
Sweaters	@ 1.10 each	26

The employee's gross pay, before deductions, is worked out as follows on the lower-priced calculator:

Example 47 *Piecework Payroll* (A)

Sequence	1	2	3	4	5
Operation	[C]	180	[×]	12	[=+]
Display	0	180	180	12	2160

[write down 21.60]

Sequence	6	7	8	9
Operation	115	[×]	32	[=+]
Display	115	115	32	3680

[write down 36.80]

Sequence	10	11	12	13
Operation	125	[×]	39	[=+]
Display	125	125	39	4875

[write down 48.75]

Sequence	14	15	16	17	18
Operation	110	[×]	26	[=+]	4875
Display	110	110	26	2860	4875

Sequence	19	20	21	22	23
Operation	[=+]	3680	[=+]	2160	[=+]
Display	7735	3680	11415	2160	13575

After steps 5, 9 and 13 the figures 21.60, 36.80 and 48.75 will have to be written down, of course.

Now, using the medium-cost calculator:

(B)

Sequence	1	2	3	4	5
Operation	[C]	1.80	[×]	12	[=]
Display	0.	1.80	1.8	12.	21.6

Sequence	6	7	8	9
Operation	1.15	[×]	32	[=]
Display	1.15	1.15	32.	36.8

Sequence	10	11	12	13
Operation	1.25	[×]	39	[=]
Display	1.25	1.25	39.	48.75

Sequence	14	15	16	17	18	19
Operation	1.10	☒	26	⊟	⊞	48.75
Display	1.10	1.10	26.	28.6	28.6	48.75

Sequence	20	21	22	23	24
Operation	⊞	36.80	⊞	21.60	⊟
Display	77.35	36.80	114.15	21.6	135.75

The reader is invited to try his hand at calculating the gross pay of a piecework employee whose completed job load for the week was as follows:

14 shirts
35 blouses
16 skirts
43 sweaters

Use the same pay rates as in the previous example. The correct answers are given in Appendix E.

6 | COMMISSIONS

There are many companies that pay their salesmen on a commission basis only, according to the volume in dollars of sales made. The rate of commission might change with each kind of product sold.

A typical commission list might be:

Product	A	752.00	@ 15%
"	B	863.00	@ 10%
"	C	400.00	@ 12%
"	D	550.00	@ 18%

The key feature is the *percentage* commission. Some hand-held calculators come with a percentage key but it is, as yet, uncommon. Where this feature is present, computing the percentage is a very easy job. However, even without a percentage button it is still easy to calculate.

For example, 15% means 15 for every 100. To find 15% of any number all we have to do is multiply it by 0.15. Here is how the gross pay can be easily calculated on the low-priced calculator for the data quoted above. Remember that one has to take into account the two decimal places when reading the answer.

Example 48 *Commissions* **(A)**

Sequence	**1**	**2**	**3**	**4**	**5**
Operation	[C]	752	[×]	15	[=+]
Display	0	752	752	15	11280

[write down 112.80]

Sequence	**6**	**7**	**8**	**9**
Operation	863	[×]	10	[=+]
Display	863	863	10	8630

[write down 86.30]

Sequence	**10**	**11**	**12**	**13**
Operation	400	[×]	12	[=+]
Display	400	400	12	4800

[write down 48.00]

Sequence	14	15	16	17	18	19
Operation	550	[×]	18	[=+]	4800	[=+]
Display	550	550	18	9900	4800	14700

Sequence	20	21	22	23
Operation	8630	[=+]	11280	[=+]
Display	8630	23330	11280	34610

The total commission earned is therefore $346.10. The same figure is, of course, arrived at by using the medium-priced calculator, as illustrated below: (B)

Sequence	1	2	3	4	5
Operation	[C]	752	[×]	.15	[=]
Display	0.	752.	752.	0.15	112.8

[write down 112.80]

Sequence	6	7	8	9
Operation	863	[×]	.10	[=]
Display	863.	863.	0.10	86.3

[write down 86.30]

Sequence	10	11	12	13
Operation	400	[×]	.12	[=]
Display	400.	400.	0.12	48.

[write down 48.00]

Sequence	14	15	16	17	18
Operation	550	[×]	.18	[=]	[+]
Display	550.	550.	0.18	99.	99.

Sequence	19	20	21	22	23	24
Operation	48.00	[+]	86.30	[+]	112.80	[=]
Display	48.00	147.	86.30	233.3	112.80	346.1

The last figure shown, 346.1, is read as $346.10, the same result as obtained above.

Here is a practice problem, similar to that just described. Calculate the gross pay according to the new data and check your results with Appendix E.

Product	A	850.00	@ 13%
"	B	642.00	@ 16%
"	C	500.00	@ 11%
"	D	480.00	@ 14%

7 | DEPRECIATION

Any time a company purchases an item that is not going to be sold as part of its finished product (such as a tape recorder, typewriter, building—even a pocket calculator) that particular item becomes an asset to the company. Taxes are paid according to the company's income and also on the total assets it owns. However, as the item ages, so does its usefulness to the company; therefore its value must be decreased in order to avoid paying taxes on the original purchase price of the item. This is what is referred to as depreciation.

The idea of depreciation is very elementary. Let us assume that a company buys a printing press for $10,000. It is expected that this printing press will have a life span of 10 years.

In calculating the depreciation, the value for the first year is considered $10,000. However, for the second year it will decrease by $1,000 to $9,000, and so on, decreasing a further $1000 for each successive year. This depreciation is charged as an expense against the company's income, thereby reducing its tax liability.

There are various ways of determining depreciation, depending, among other things, on the type of item involved. We shall illustrate only the case cited above, using different figures. The method is known as the straight-line method.

Cost of printing press	$10,462.00
Scrap value	500.00

The formula is:

$$\text{annual depreciation} = \frac{\text{cost price} - \text{scrap value}}{\text{number of periods}}$$

In our case, assuming its life span to be 12 years, it is:

$$\frac{10{,}462 - 500}{12}$$

Example 49 *Straight-Line Depreciation* (A)

Sequence	**1**	**2**	**3**	**4**	**5**
Operation	[C]	10462	[=+]	500	[−]
Display	0	10462	10462	500	9962

Sequence	6	7	8	9
Operation	[÷]	12	[=+]	[▶]
Display	9962	12	830	166666

The depreciation is therefore $830.17 per year. Now, using the medium-priced calculator:

(B)

Sequence	1	2	3	4	5	6	7
Operation	[C]	10462	[−]	500	[÷]	12	[=]
Display	0.	10462.	10462.	−500.	9962.	12.	830.16666

A chart could be made of the current value and the amount of depreciation. It would look like the following chart, which has been left incomplete. The reader might like to complete it. Appendix E shows the answers.

Age	Periodic Depreciation	Depreciated Value	Total Accumulated Depreciation
0	......	10,462.	0
1	830.	9,632.	830.
2	830.	8,802.	1660.
3	......	......	......
4	......	......	......
5	......	......	......
6	......	......	......
7	......	......	......
8	......	......	......
9	......	......	......
10	......	......	......
11	......	......	......
12	......	......	......

A retailer buys 362 toys at $5.75 each, expecting to sell them at $11.00 each. However, owing to an accident they were all slightly damaged and he was forced to sell them at $4.25 each. What is the retailer's loss on sales?

The problem can be solved in two ways:

$$362 \times (5.75 - 4.25)$$

or

$$(362 \times 5.75) - (362 \times 4.25)$$

We shall solve it by the first method, first with the lower-priced calculator:

Example 50 *Sales Profit and Loss* (A)

Sequence	1	2	3	4	5
Operation	[C]	575	[=+]	425	[−]
Display	0	575	575	425	150

Sequence	6	7	8
Operation	[×]	362	[=+]
Display	150	362	54300

Since we must move the decimal point two places to the left, the correct answer is $543.00, which represents the loss on sales. Using the medium-priced calculator: (B)

Sequence	1	2	3	4	5	6	7
Operation	[C]	5.75	[−]	4.25	[×]	362	[=]
Display	0	5.75	5.75	−4.25	1.5	362.	543.

Here are some practice problems to work on:

(1) A bakery makes 1,020 loaves at a cost of 12¢ per loaf. They are sold to a retailer, who buys them at 20¢ each. The shipping cost of $85 is paid by the bakery. What is the result of the transaction in terms of profit or loss?

(2) A factory makes a product whose average cost is $1.05. It sells them in quantity to 3 different stores as follows:

405 @ $3.25
360 @ $3.35
310 @ $3.43

Assuming the trucking charges total $53.10, what was the net gain or loss to the factory?

Answers are in Appendix E.

9 | RETAILING

One of the basic notions in retailing is that of markup. Percentage markup is based on the cost and is arrived at by the following formula:

$$\text{percentage markup} = \frac{(\text{selling price} - \text{cost price})}{\text{cost price}} \times 100$$

Suppose an article which sells for $200.00 costs the dealer $125.00. We can calculate the percentage markup by:

$$\text{Percentage markup} = \frac{200 - 125}{125} \times 100$$

Example 51 *Percentage Markup* (A)

Sequence	**1**	**2**	**3**	**4**	**5**	**6**
Operation	[C]	200	[=+]	125	[−]	[×]
Display	0	200	200	125	75	75

Sequence	**7**	**8**	**9**	**10**
Operation	100	[÷]	125	[=+]
Display	100	7500	125	60

The result shows a percentage markup of 60%. This is confirmed by the medium-priced calculator.

(B)

Sequence	**1**	**2**	**3**	**4**	**5**	**6**	**7**	**8**	**9**
Operation	C	200	[−]	125	[÷]	125	[×]	100	[=]
Display	0.	200.	200.	−125.	75.	125.	.6	100.	60.

5

YOUR CAR

Anyone owning an automobile or contemplating the purchase of one will find a calculator a most useful friend, much more reliable than the average used-car salesman.

1 | BUYING AN AUTOMOBILE

For our first example let us consider the problem of trading in your old car for a new one. Let us say you want to buy a car costing $4,567 and you're trading in your present car for which you are allowed $1,789.

The dealer offers you a plan whereby you can pay off your debt by a monthly payment of $270 spread over twelve months. The question is: is it worthwhile to go along with the dealer's plan or is it more economical for you to take out an auto loan for one year at the local bank, where the interest rate is 7½%?

First, we must calculate the cost of the new car with the trade-in taken into consideration.

$$\text{cost of new car} = \$4,567 - \$1,789 = \$2,778$$

Going along with the dealer's suggested plan, you would have to pay

$$12 \times \$270 = \$3,240$$

Therefore, the cost of the loan, according to this plan, is

$$\$3,240 - \$2,778 = \$462$$

Now we have to determine how much interest would have to be paid if the bank loan is made. In other words, how much is 7½ % of $2,778?

Using the calculator we find that this amount is $208.35. Obviously, the bank's interest is considerably lower than the dealer's and therefore the bank loan would represent a savings of

$$\$462.00 - \$208.35 = \$253.65$$

Another way of asking the same kind of question is: What percentage of $2,778 is $462, the interest the dealer would get?

Again using the calculator we compute

$$\frac{462}{2778} \times 100$$

getting a result of 16.63%. We shall illustrate only the last portion of this problem.

Example 52 *Auto-Purchase Plan* (A)

Sequence	**1**	**2**	**3**	**4**	**5**
Operation	[C]	462	[×]	100	[÷]
Display	0	462	462	100	46200

Sequence	**6**	**7**	**8**
Operation	2778	[=+]	[▶]
Display	2778	16	630669

Or using the medium-priced calculator:

(B)

Sequence	1	2	3	4	5	6	7
Operation	[C]	462	[×]	100	[÷]	2778	[=]
Display	0.	462.	462.	100.	46200.	2778.	16.630669

2 | AUTOMOBILE SERVICE

Most dealers and service stations charge a flat rate for repair work. If, for example, a customer brings in his car for a tune-up, the labor charge is established by looking in a *Flat Rate Manual* to determine how many hours the job is rated to take. If the job is listed in the manual to take 1½ hours and the service charge is $5.00 per hour, the customer will be charged $7.50 for labor, plus the parts, if any, for the tune-up. The mechanic who works on the job will be paid for the 1½ hours regardless of whether he finishes in ½ hour or 2½ hours.

The service manager generally assigns the flat rate to the service tickets while the parts department enters the quantity and price of all parts used.

For the purposes of this problem let us assume that the bill of repairs reads as follows:

Parts:

8 plugs @	$ .78	$6.24
points	2.15	2.15
condenser	1.25	1.25
rotor	2.75	2.75
PCV valve	1.75	1.75
		$14.14

Labor:

$5 per hour;
1½ hours

	7.50	
		21.64
plus 7% tax		2.51
	Total	$24.15

However, there is an error in the above table. Can you, with the aid of your calculator, spot the error?

Example 53 *Automobile Service Bill* (A)

Sequence	1	2	3	4	5	6	7
Operation	[C]	8	[×]	78	[=+]	215	[=+]
Display	0	8	8	78	624	215	839

Sequence	8	9	10	11	12	13
Operation	125	[=+]	275	[=+]	175	[=+]
Display	125	964	275	1239	175	1414

This figure of $14.14 agrees with the bill, so the error is yet to be found. Now let's check the labor charge.

Sequence	14	15	16	17
Operation	15	[×]	5	[=+]
Display	15	15	5	75

This gives the figure of $7.50 for the labor charge, which is also correct. Now let us compute the total by simply adding the charge for parts to the labor cost.

Sequence	**18**	**19**	**20**	**21**	**22**
Operation	[C]	1414	[=+]	750	
Display	0	1414	1414	750	2164

The answer of $21.64 also agrees with the bill. To this total we have to add 7% tax.

Here we have two alternatives. Either we can multiply $21.64 by .07 and compute the tax itself, which comes to $1.51, or multiply $21.64 by 1.07 and arrive at the inclusive charge of $23.15. Either way, the cost of the repairs should be $23.15, not $24.15.

Here is the complete schematic using the medium-priced calculator.

(B)

Sequence	**1**	**2**	**3**	**4**	**5**
Operation	[C]	8	[×]	.78	[+]
Display	0.	8.	8.	.78	6.24
Sequence	**6**	**7**	**8**	**9**	**10**
Operation	2.15	[+]	1.25	[+]	2.75
Display	2.15	8.39	1.25	9.64	2.75

Sequence	11	12	13	14	15
Operation	[+]	1.75	[+]	7.50	[×]
Display	12.39	1.75	14.14	7.50	21.64

Sequence	16	17
Operation	1.07	[=]
Display	1.07	23.1548

6

INTEREST ON MONEY

Interest is nothing more than the income derived from invested capital. In other words, it is the fee paid for having the use of money. The sum of money loaned is called the *principal*. An agreement is generally made about the time period for which the money is loaned. The name given to the sum of money returned to the lender at the end of his time period, i.e., the principal plus the interest, is called the *amount*.

1 | SIMPLE INTEREST

Let us say that a company secures a loan from a bank for $2,000, payable in one year, and has to pay the bank an interest charge of $100. What rate of interest does this represent? One need merely resort to the following simple formula:

$$r = \frac{i}{pt}$$

where:

r = rate of interest (what we want to find)
i = amount of interest ($100)
p = principal ($2,000)
t = time in years (1 year)

We find the value of r by calculating the expression on the right of the equal sign, keying in 100 for i, 2000 for p, and since $t = 1$ in this case we can conveniently ignore it.

Example 54 *Finding the Interest Rate* (A)

Sequence	**1**	**2**	**3**	**4**	**5**	**6**
Operation	[C]	100	[÷]	2000	[=+]	[►]
Display	0	100	100	2000		0 050000

The calculated result is

0.05

which is the same as 5%. Here is the schematic using the medium-priced calculator:

(B)

Sequence	**1**	**2**	**3**	**4**	**5**
Operation	[C]	100	[÷]	2000	[=]
Display	0.	100.	100.	2000.	.05

From the equation just used, we can compute any of the four quantities, whichever one is unknown, by simply selecting the appropriate form of the equation. The other three are:

$$i = prt$$

$$p = \frac{i}{rt}$$

$$t = \frac{i}{pr}$$

Each of these four versions of the same equation relates to what is called *simple interest*. Simple interest is always given on a yearly basis. If months are involved, the number of months must be divided by 12 to get the value of t. If the time is given in days one usually divides the number of days by 360, giving what is called *ordinary simple interest,* as opposed to the *exact simple interest* that is calculated by dividing the number of days by 365 (or 366 during a leap year).

Let us now do a series of such problems.

Find the exact simple interest and the amount if $500 is loaned for 100 days at 4%.

To solve for i, we use the formula:

$$i = prt$$

where $p = 500$, $r = 4\%$ and $t = 100/365$.

Example 55 *Exact Simple Interest* (A)

Sequence	**1**	**2**	**3**	**4**	**5**
Operation	C	500	×	4	×
Display	0	500	500	4	2000
Sequence	**6**	**7**	**8**	**9**	**10**
Operation	100	÷	365	=+	►
Display	100	200000	365	547	945205

This yields a result for the interest of $5.48. The amount is $500.00 + $5.48 = $505.48.

A man who invested $1,000 had $1,010 returned to him 45 days later. At what rate did the money earn ordinary simple interest?

$$\begin{aligned} \text{amount} &= 1010 \\ \text{principal} &= 1000 \\ \text{interest} &= 10 \\ \text{time} &= 45 \text{ days} \\ r &= ? \end{aligned}$$

$$r = \frac{i}{pt}$$

$$r = \frac{10}{1000 \times \frac{45}{360}}$$

Example 56 *Ordinary Simple Interest* (A)

Sequence	1	2	3	4	5	6
Operation	[C]	1000	[×]	45	[÷]	360
Display	0	1000	1000	45	45000	360

Sequence	7		8	9	10
Operation	[=+]	[write down 125]	10	[÷]	125
Display	125		10	10	125

Sequence	11	12
Operation	[=+]	[▶]
Display	0	080000

The result is 0.08, or 8%, a figure that is confirmed by the medium-priced calculator:

(B)

Sequence	1	2	3	4	5	6	7
Operation	[C]	1000	[×]	45	[÷]	360	[=]
Display	0.	1000.	1000.	45.	45000.	360.	125.

[write down 125]

Sequence	8	9	10	11
Operation	10	[÷]	125	[=]
Display	10.	10.	125.	.08

Here are some sample problems for the reader to solve. The correct answers are given in Appendix E.

(1) Find the simple interest on a loan of $1,850 @ 6¾% for 95 days.

(2) Find the ordinary and exact simple interest on $2,500 for 90 days @ 5% in a normal year.

(3) What principal will amount to $2,050 in 6 months if the rate is 5%?

(4) How many days will it take for $900 to earn $6 if it is invested at 5¼% ordinary simple interest?

2 | COMPOUND INTEREST

When interest is periodically added to the principal and this *new sum* is used as the principal for the following time period, the interest will be greater than it would be if invested in simple interest, because interest is paid on the *compounded* amount. This is therefore known as *compound interest.*

The time period between two consecutive interest computations is called the *interest period* and may be any convenient length of time such as a month, 3 months, 6 months, a year or even a day.

The interest rate is usually quoted on a yearly basis and must be changed to the interest rate *per interest period* for purposes of computation.

Let us take an elementary example to explain this concept. A man deposits the sum of $1000 in the bank for one year at the rate of 8%, compounded quarterly. This means that after the first quarter, 2% (one-quarter of 8%) is added to the principal. Interest for the second three months is computed using this total as the new principal. Here is a chart illustrating how the money "grows":

Payment Period	Principal	Interest	New Principal
0			1000.00
1	1000.00	20.00	1020.00
2	1020.00	20.40	1040.40
3	1040.40	20.81	1061.21
4	1061.21	21.22	1082.43

Thus we see—and you can easily confirm this with your calculator—that compounded quarterly at 8%, $1,000 becomes $1,082.43 at the end of one year. This compares with $1,080, which is the amount that $1,000 would have become if invested at simple interest. The difference is $2.43.

We are fortunate in that there is a fundamental formula for computing compound interest. It is

$$S = P(1 + i)^n$$

where S is the final amount, P is the principal, i is the interest rate per compound period and n is the number of interest periods.

Referring once again to the example above:

$$S = 1000\ (1 + .02)^4$$

Let us now compute the value for S using the low-priced calculator.

Example 57 *Compound Interest* (A)

Sequence	1	2	3	4	5	6	7
Operation	[C]	102	[×]	[=+]	[×]	[=+]	[►]
Display	0	102	102	10404	10404	108243	216

(You will recall that in order to square a number the [×] button is depressed followed by the [=+] button.)

The final figure in the display is

108243216

Positioning the decimal point to the left eight places and to the right three places gives the result

1082.43

The reader will be more convinced using the medium-priced calculator, where we shall take advantage of the constant feature. So, with the constant switch on:

(B)

Sequence	1	2	3	4	5
Operation	[C]	1.02	[×]	[=]	[=]
Display	0.	1.02	1.02	1.0404	1.061208

Sequence	6	7	8	9
Operation	[=]	[×]	1000	[=]
Display	1.0824321	1.0824321	1000.	1082.4321

The answer of $1,082.43 is immediately confirmed.

Here are some practice problems on compound interest.

(1) If $8,300 is invested at 6¼% compounded quarterly for 2 years, what is the compounded amount?

(2) Find the compounded amount that $1000 will reach if invested at 5.4% and compounded semiannually for 3 years.

3 | PERPETUITIES

A perpetuity is an annuity whose payments are to continue forever.

Suppose, for example, a man wishes to prepare for his retirement. Upon careful reflection he decides that after the age of 65 he will be able to live comfortably on $1,200 every 3 months. How much money invested at 6% will he have to save in order to ensure an income of $1,200 every 3 months, no matter how long he lives?

Since the man in question does not know how long he is going to live, the payments must be derived from the interest on the principal, leaving the principal untouched. Thus he assures himself of an infinite number of monthly payments.

The formula for the amount, A, to be invested, the interest rate per period i, and the perpetuity payment, R, is surprisingly simple:

$$A = \frac{R}{i}$$

from which, given any two, we can easily compute the other one.

In the example cited above,

$$A = \frac{1200}{.015}$$

This should not be too difficult to calculate on a lower-priced calculator.

Example 58 *Perpetuity* (A)

Sequence	**1**	**2**	**3**	**4**	**5**	**6**
Operation	[C]	1200	[÷]	15	[=+]	[►]
Display	0	1200	1200	15	80	000000

Since we divided by 15 rather than by .015, the decimal point in the answer 80.000000 has to be moved 3 places to the right, giving the result $80,000.

Here is the schematic for the medium-priced calculator.

(B)

Sequence	**1**	**2**	**3**	**4**	**5**
Operation	[C]	1200	[÷]	.015	[=]
Display	0.	1200.	1200.	.015	80000.

Here are some practice problems.

(1) How much money will it require to establish a permanent scholarship paying $850 at the end of each year if the money can be invested at a guaranteed 4%?

(2) At what rate of interest will $68,000 have to be invested to ensure an income of $10,000 a year in perpetuity?

$\left(\text{Hint: } i = \frac{R}{A}\right)$

(3) What income will be guaranteed in perpetuity by investing \$50,000 at 8%?

(Hint: $R = Ai$)

7

PROBLEMS FOR STUDENTS

The problems we have discussed so far are of interest to students and nonstudents. What we propose to cover now are additional problems that often are encountered in the classroom.

1 | RECIPROCALS

A favorite type of school problem in mathematics is the following:

If a certain faucet can fill a tub in 2 hours and another can fill it in 3 hours, how long will it take to fill the tub if they are both turned on simultaneously?

If faucet A fills the bath in 2 hours, in one hour it fills one-half of the tub.

Similarly, faucet B, which alone takes 3 hours to fill the tub, in one hour will fill one-third of the tub.

Faucet A in 1 hour fills $\frac{1}{2}$ of tub
Faucet B in 1 hour fills $\frac{1}{3}$ of tub

Now, if they are both turned on simultaneously, in one hour

$$\frac{1}{2} + \frac{1}{3}$$

of the tub will be filled.

$$\frac{1}{2} + \frac{1}{3} = \frac{5}{6}$$

Now, if it takes one hour to fill 5/6 of the tub, it will require 1/5 of an hour (12 minutes) to fill 1/6 of the tub.

It therefore follows that in order to fill 6/6 of the tub, i.e., the whole tub, it will require $6 \times 1/5$ hour or 6/5 of an hour, which is 1 hour 12 minutes.

This kind of problem involves the calculation of the *reciprocal* of a number—that is, 1 divided by that number. The reciprocal of 2 is ½; similarly, the reciprocal of 3 is ⅓. Some of the latest model calculators have a reciprocal button.

Adding ½ + ⅓ is easy, even without a calculator—just add 2 and 3 and then multiply 2 and 3 and divide the first by the second. (This works only for two fractions that are reciprocals.) Thus we get 5/6. Taking the reciprocal of a fraction means inverting it—6/5 of an hour is our correct result.

We shall now solve some problems involving reciprocals, using the low- and medium-priced calculators.

(1) If one man can fill a sack in 52 minutes and another in 40 minutes, how many minutes will it take if they work simultaneously?

$$\frac{1}{52} + \frac{1}{40} = ?$$

We can calculate this by two different methods in order to confirm the accuracy of the results. One way is to find the sum by adding 52 and 40 and then multiplying 52 and 40, dividing the first answer by the second. Or we can compute the reciprocal of each number separately and then add the two results.

Sequence	**1**	**2**	**3**	**4**	**5**
Operation	[C]	52	[=+]	40	[=+]
Display	0	52	52	40	92
					[write down 92]

Sequence	**6**	**7**	**8**	**9**
Operation	52	[×]	40	[=+]
Display	52	52	40	2080
				[write down 2080]

Sequence	**10**	**11**	**12**	**13**	**14**
Operation	92	[÷]	2080	[=+]	[►]
Display	92	92	2080	0	044230

Thus we get 0.044230

We confirm this result by calculating the reciprocal of 52 (by keying in 1 and dividing by 52) and adding it to the reciprocal of 40. You will find this comes to

$$\begin{array}{r} 0.019230 \\ +\ 0.025000 \\ \hline 0.044230 \end{array}$$

(The reciprocal of 0.044230 is 22.6.)

All we have to do now, using the inexpensive calculator, is to invert the fraction

$$\frac{92}{2080} \text{ to } \frac{2080}{92}$$

Sequence	15	16	17	18	19
Operation	2080	[÷]	92	[=+]	[►]
Display	2080	2080	92	22	608695

Our answer is therefore 22.6 minutes.

Using the medium-priced calculator, we shall actually calculate the reciprocals.

(B)

Sequence	1	2	3	4		5
Operation	[C]	1	[÷]	52		[=] [write down
Display	0.	1.	1.	52.	0.0192307	0.0192307]

Sequence	6	7	8	9	10	11
Operation	1	[÷]	40	[=]	[+]	0.0192307
Display	1.	1.	40.	0.025	0.025	0.0192307

Sequence	12		
Operation	[=]	[write down 0.0442307]	[we want its reciprocal]
Display	0.0442307		

Sequence	13	14	15	16
Operation	1	[÷]	.0442307	[=]
Display	1.	1.	0.0442307	22.608731

Thus our answer of 22.6 minutes is confirmed.

2 | A TECHNIQUE FOR CALCULATING RECIPROCALS

If the pocket calculator contains a constant feature, there is a far better way to calculate a reciprocal. If the number whose reciprocal is wanted is *n*, then its reciprocal $1/n$ can be found by the following procedure:

switch on constant key
enter *n*
depress [÷]
depress [=]
depress [=]

This technique takes advantage of the fact that any number divided by itself gives 1. This 1 is now automatically placed in the display and since the constant factor is the original number entered, the reciprocal is obtained immediately. Try it—you'll find it works beautifully.

Reciprocals are also encountered in physics. When two (or more) resistors are connected in parallel, the total equivalent resistance is given by the formula:

$$\frac{1}{R_{total}} = \frac{1}{R_1} + \frac{1}{R_2}$$

For the case of, say, 5 resistors,

$$\frac{1}{R_{total}} = \frac{1}{R_1} + \frac{1}{R_2} + \frac{1}{R_3} + \frac{1}{R_4} + \frac{1}{R_5}$$

In engineering, too, one often needs to know the reciprocal of the sum of reciprocals. Suppose, for example, the total equivalent resistance of three resistors in parallel is wanted. We know that the formula for this is:

$$\frac{1}{R_{total}} = \frac{1}{R_1} + \frac{1}{R_2} + \frac{1}{R_3}$$

Suppose

$$R_1 = 12$$
$$R_2 = 26$$
$$R_3 = 34$$

Here is the schematic for calculating the total equivalent resistance with the medium-priced calculator only. We could not get sufficient accuracy with the fixed-point, cheaper model.

Example 60 Equivalent Resistance in Parallel (B)

Sequence	**1**	**2**	**3**	**4**	**5**
Operation	[C]	1	[÷]	12	[=]
Display	0.	1.	1.	12.	0.0833333

[write down .0833333]

Sequence	**6**	**7**	**8**	**9**
Operation	1	[÷]	26	[=]
Display	1.	1.	26.	0.0384615

[write down .0384615]

Sequence	**10**	**11**	**12**	**13**
Operation	1	[÷]	34	[=]
Display	1.	1.	34.	0.0294117

Sequence	**14**	**15**	**16**
Operation	[+]	.0384615	[+]
Display	.0294117	0.0384615	0.0678732

Sequence	17		18	19	20
Operation	.0833333	switch to constant mode	÷	=	=
Display	.0833333		0.1512065	1.	6.6134723

Thus we arrive at a result of 6.61.

Here are two practice problems using the concept of reciprocals. Remember that if your calculator has a reciprocal function, feel free to use it instead of computing the reciprocal as we have done. Answers are in Appendix E.

(1) It takes worker A 45 minutes to dig a trench. Worker B can do it in 30 minutes; worker C takes 52 minutes. How long would it take if they all worked together?

(2) Four resistances of 21, 24, 30 and 36 ohms respectively are connected in parallel. What is the total resistance?

3 | TEMPERATURE CONVERSION

The formula by means of which it is possible to convert temperature from Fahrenheit to Centigrade and vice versa is

$$\frac{C}{5} = \frac{F-32}{9}$$

Using this general formula, one merely inserts whichever is known—either C or F—and calculates the other. For simplicity, one may take this formula and write down two separate formulas:

$$C = \frac{5F-160}{9}$$

$$F = \frac{9C+160}{5}$$

If one knows the *F* temperature, one substitutes it in the first formula above and calculates *C*. If *C* is known, one substitutes it in the second formula and calculates *F*.

Let us try an example or two.

Convert 98.4°F to its equivalent Centigrade temperature.

Example 61 98.4°F = ?°C (A)

Sequence	**1**	**2**	**3**	**4**	**5**
Operation	[C]	5	[×]	984	[=+]
Display	0	5	5	984	4920

[re-enter 492 after clearing calculator]

Sequence	**6**	**7**	**8**	**9**	**10**
Operation	492	[=+]	160	[−]	[÷]
Display	492	492	160	332	332

Sequence	**11**	**12**	**13**
Operation	9	[=+]	[►]
Display	9	36	888888

Here we get an answer of 36.89°C, the correct result. We had to be careful to re-enter the correct product of 5 × 98.4, i.e., 492. With the low-priced calculator, of course, we were forced to multiply by 984, and had we used the figure of 4920 from which to subtract 160, our result would have been erroneous. This trouble is circumvented using the floating-point, medium-priced calculator.

(B)

Sequence	1	2	3	4	5	6	7
Operation	[C]	5	[×]	98.4	[−]	160	[÷]
Display	0.	5.	5.	98.4	492.	−160.	332.

Sequence	8	9
Operation	9	[=]
Display	9.	36.888888

Now let us do a conversion from Centigrade to Fahrenheit, first using the lower-priced calculator. Our example concerns the boiling point of water.

Example 62 100°C = ?°F (A)

Sequence	1	2	3	4	5
Operation	[C]	9	[×]	100	[=+]
Display	0	9	9	100	900

Sequence	6	7	8	9	10
Operation	160	[=+]	[÷]	5	[=+]
Display	160	1060	1060	5	212

Thus we get the correct answer, 212°F, a result confirmed by the medium-priced calculator.

(B)

Sequence	1	2	3	4	5	6	7	8	9
Operation	[C]	9	[×]	100	[+]	160	[÷]	5	[=]
Display	0.	9.	9.	100.	900.	160.	1060.	5.	212.

Here are some practice problems for you in conversion of temperature.

Convert the following Centigrade temperatures to Fahrenheit:

(1) 42°C
(2) 65°C
(3) –40°C
(4) 0°C

Convert the following Fahrenheit temperatures to Centigrade:

(1) 48°F
(2) 60.123°F
(3) –40°F
(4) 0°F

4 | CONVERSION TO THE METRIC SYSTEM

The previous problem involved the conversion of temperature from one scale to another. In the United States, temperatures are invariably given in Fahrenheit. This was also the case in Britain but, with an eye to the inevitable future, the United Kingdom is now committed to a 12-year program toward a complete changeover to the metric system. Now they broadcast temperatures in both scales to help ease the eventual conversion.

In the U.S. Congress there are currently more than a dozen bills that would pave the way for the adoption of the metric system.* Already thousands of American manufacturers who have seen the handwriting on the wall are converting to the metric system. The United States is almost alone in its usage of feet, pints and pounds rather than meters, liters and kilograms. Only Canada and a few

* Gerd Wilcke, "Here Comes the Metric System," *The New York Times,* June 24, 1973.

small countries like Sierra Leone and Barbados still measure according to the nonmetric system.

The need to "go metric" was seen as far back as 1866 when Congress passed an act permitting the use of the metric system in the U.S. However, the current pressure to convert did not really get started until August 1968 when the government undertook a three-year study of the impact of the increasing worldwide use of the metric system. The result of this study was a report entitled *A Metric America—A Decision Whose Time has Come.*

In August 1972 the Senate passed a metric bill. Since it was not acted upon by the House it died with the 92nd Congress. In 1973 the House was confronted by the metric bills, submitted by fifty representatives. A conversion to the metric system is of considerable magnitude. It is estimated that for the United States to convert to the metric system the expense involved would be between a few billion and a few hundred billion dollars.

Here are some *approximate* conversions to and from metric measures as given by a U.S. Department of Commerce information document.* The first chart shows conversions to metric measures, the second from metric measures. The pocket calculator is obviously a handy tool for making such conversions during this transition period.

Symbol	When You Know	Multiply by	To Find	Symbol
		LENGTH		
in	inches	2.5	centimeters	cm
ft	feet	30	centimeters	cm
yd	yards	0.9	meters	m
mi	miles	1.6	kilometers	km

* U.S. Government Printing Office, Stock Number 0303-0168.

Symbol	When You Know	Multiply by	To Find	Symbol
		AREA		
in^2	square inches	6.5	square centimeters	cm^2
ft^2	square feet	0.09	square meters	m^2
yd^2	square yards	0.8	square meters	m^2
mi^2	square miles	2.6	square kilometers	km^2
	acres	0.4	hectares	ha
		MASS (weight)		
oz	ounces	28	grams	g
lb	pounds	0.45	kilograms	kg
	short tons (2000 lbs)	0.9	tonnes	t
		VOLUME		
tsp	teaspoons	5	milliliters	ml
tbsp	tablespoons	15	milliliters	ml
fl oz	fluid ounces	30	milliliters	ml
c	cups	0.24	liters	l
pt	pints	0.47	liters	l
qt	quarts	0.95	liters	l
gal	gallons	3.8	liters	l
ft^3	cubic feet	0.03	cubic meters	m^3
yd^3	cubic yards	0.76	cubic meters	m^3
		LENGTH		
mm	millimeters	0.04	inches	in
cm	centimeters	0.4	inches	in
m	meters	3.3	feet	ft
m	meters	1.1	yards	yd
km	kilometers	0.6	miles	mi

Symbol	When You Know	Multiply by	To Find	Symbol
		AREA		
cm^2	square centimeters	0.16	square inches	in^2
m^2	square meters	1.2	square yards	yd^2
km^2	square kilometers	0.4	square miles	mi^2
ha	hectares (10,000 m^2)	2.5	acres	
		VOLUME		
ml	milliliters	0.03	fluid ounces	fl oz
l	liters	2.1	pints	pt
l	liters	1.06	quarts	qt
l	liters	0.26	gallons	gal
m^3	cubic meters	35	cubic feet	ft^3
m^3	cubic meters	1.3	cubic yards	yd^3

5 | CONVERSION OF KILOMETERS

Travelling along the highways of Europe one never sees distances expressed in miles, but rather in kilometers. The relation between the two units is as follows:

$$1 \text{ kilometer} = 0.621 \text{ miles}$$

Suppose we wanted to convert a reading of 71 kilometers to miles. All we would have to do is to multiply 71 by 0.621, giving us 44.091 miles.

This represents a distance of somewhat more than 44 miles. (It is possible, of course, to determine how many yards, feet and inches the fraction 0.091 of a mile represents. Just remember that there are 1760 yards to the mile, 3 feet to the yard and 12 inches to the foot.)

Example 63 85 kilometers = ? miles (A)

Sequence	1	2	3	4	5
Operation	[C]	85	[×]	621	[=+]
Display	0	85	85	621	52785

This conversion, done on the lower-priced calculator, reads as 52.785 miles. Using the constant feature of the medium-priced calculator, we can with very little effort calculate the equivalent of many distances expressed in kilometers. Let us take the following:

85 kilometers
102 kilometers
469 kilometers
5 kilometers

With the constant switch in operation: (B)

Sequence	1	2	3	4	5
Operation	[C]	85	[×]	.621	[=]
Display	0.	85.	85.	0.621	52.785

Sequence	6	7	8	9	10	11
Operation	102	[=]	469	[=]	5	[=]
Display	102.	63.342	469.	291.249	5.	3.105

Thus we can find with ease the following equivalents:

85 km = 52.785 mi
102 km = 63.342 mi
469 km = 291.249 mi
5 km = 3.105 mi

8

THE HIGH-PRICED CALCULATOR

For obvious reasons most of the contents of this book relate to those pocket calculators which are within reach of most of us. The two types we have discussed in some detail are the low-priced calculator, costing around $50 at today's prices, and the medium-priced calculator at around $100. It would be a serious omission—if not downright misleading—to say nothing about the high-priced pocket calculators that are presently selling at $300 and $400.

Along with their greater cost and almost unbelievable computational power and speed, these calculators are stylish in design, shirtpocket-sized and lightweight.

There are basically two such extraordinary computer calculators on the market today, both made by the same company. The HP-35 is the scientist's and engineer's dream pocket calculator. It sold initially for $400 and only recently was reduced by $100. The manufacturer has now come out with a "souped-up" version, the HP-45, also intended for the scientist-engineer type, one who needs instantaneous solutions of problems for which the other pocket calculators are inadequate.

The same company has produced a businessman's version of the calculator, called the HP-80, at $400. It not only performs all the standard arithmetic functions one expects of a calculator, but among many other features

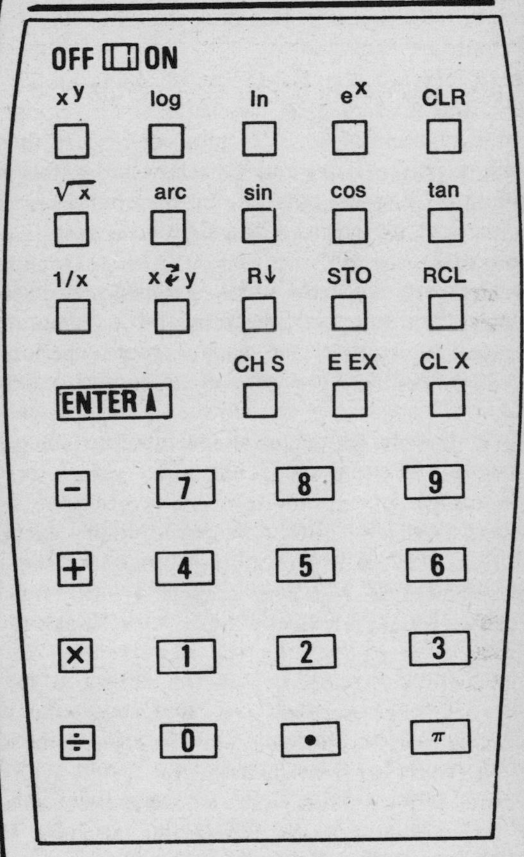

HP-35 Keyboard

calculates percentages, running totals, number of days between any two given dates, future date given the number of days, future value of an amount compounded, present value of a compounded amount, future value of an annuity, effective rate of a mortgage and linear-regression (trend line) analysis.

The 35 keys of the HP-35 permit logarithmic, trigonometric and mathematical calculations, displaying up to 10 significant decimal digits. It goes one step further than full floating point by not only correctly and automatically positioning the decimal point during the course of a calculation, but also permitting a calculating range of—believe it or not—10^{-99} to 10^{99}.

This calculator does the usual arithmetic operations of addition, subtraction, multiplication and division, and includes another feature, the square root function, that appears only on the more expensive medium-priced models.

As a brief glance at the keyboard will indicate, the HP-35 can handle trigonometric calculations since it has the capability of sin *x*, cos *x*, tan *x*, arc sin *x*, arc cos *x*, and arc tan *x*.

It can handle logarithms too. Not just to base 10 but also to base *e*—and even e^x. In addition to these it can raise a number to any power, compute reciprocals instantly and also gives the value of π with the stroke of a button.

An important advance is that the HP-35 is provided with an "operational stack" of four registers, plus a memory register for constants. The stack is used for solving problems that require intermediate results and at the appropriate time, automatically bringing them back for further processing. This eliminates the need for scratch notes and the re-entry of intermediate answers.

Numbers may be entered on the HP-35 in either floating

point or so-called scientific notation. Answers larger than 10^{-2} and smaller than 10^{10} are displayed in regular floating point with the decimal properly positioned. For values outside of this range, answers are displayed in scientific notation, with the exponent of 10 shown at the right of the display.

Obviously, a whole book could be written about these high-priced pocket calculators and their methods of operation. What we have said here about one of them, the HP-35, covers this model only superficially. It is not within the province of this book to go into the details of operation of this extremely useful and sophisticated pocket calculator.

9

THE "NEW MATH" AND THE POCKET CALCULATOR

The modern American high school student has almost certainly been raised on the so-called "new math." Investigations are currently in progress to determine how the understanding of today's student of mathematics compares with that of the student of ten years ago. Judging by preliminary findings, the concepts of the "new math" were easily acquired by today's student, but unlike the student of a decade ago he generally has difficulty managing the elementary drills of multiplication and division and the like. Even though a good argument could be made for the fact that the modern student's appreciation of the science of mathematics and his general familiarity with number systems is much better, nevertheless, to an increasing extent he is unable to master the mechanical skills of calculation.

Some of those involved in the development of the "new math" are now having second thoughts. Not only did it not solve any problems, they feel, but it actually did harm. Such fears are backed by the ever-worsening test scores of arithmetic students across the nation. Whatever the merits of the "new math," if children are graduating without knowing how to add, subtract, multiply and divide using just a pencil and paper, something is wrong. As a result of this realization those in positions of responsibility are revising both the elementary and secondary modern mathematics programs. There is now a tendency to veer away from the study of mathematics just for the sheer beauty of the subject toward an emphasis on basic skills. Few will argue that our everyday life necessitates the need to know how to do simple arithmetic accurately. Although a knowledge of set theory and number systems (upon which much of the "new math" is based) is all very well, it is felt that this could easily be dispensed with if it has to be learned at the expense of the more basic skills.

One senior editor of mathematics texts feels that the "new math" is not worth the pains it imposed upon the student. He made the observation that parents, most of whom are thoroughly unfamiliar with the concepts of the "new math," should be able to pick up their child's textbook and not only understand it, but also be able to help the child with the homework.

The "new math" has been severely criticized as a hoax perpetrated by charlatans and entrepreneurs of the 1960s. A noted New York University professor of mathematics agrees with this scathing charge and goes on to admonish them for not having done some preliminary intensive testing under closely supervised teaching conditions before flooding the market with "materials and programs of unproven worth. Instead, they just rushed the stuff into the schools. It was irresponsible educational innovation." *

Perhaps, as others point out, the success of the "new math" is heavily dependent upon the teacher. The more

* Richard Martin, "Many Schools Discover Kids Using 'New Math' Can't Divide 100 by 10," *The Wall Street Journal*, May 31, 1973.

math-oriented the teacher, the better the teaching and the more effective the learning process.

It seems to be the consensus that on the secondary school level major changes will be made in an attempt to bring relevancy, practical applications and vocationally oriented mathematics into the classroom.

As a first step, at Columbia University's Teachers College a $1.2-million secondary school improvement project has been undertaken to develop a completely revamped curriculum. It will be a unified one, combining algebra, geometry, trigonometry, calculus, probability, statistics and other subjects usually taught in high school and college. It envisions a program where, by the time a student reaches the 10th grade, most of the long-winded calculations will be programmed by the student on an electronic computer. Computers, however, are very expensive.

The advent of the hand-held electronic calculator may change even these very recent plans. What five years ago was unpredictable is now a conspicuous reality. For the price of an ordinary bicycle one can buy what amounts to a personal computer, capable of instant computation with unbelievable accuracy and speed.

Of course, some claim that an electronic calculator is liable to play the role of an educational crutch in the hands of a school child. But if he is permitted to *check* his answers with the calculator it could be an important educational tool. Perhaps an electronic calculator should be a permanent fixture on every first- and second-grader's desk. It has the distinct advantage of permitting the slow student to repeat a process as often as he needs while at the same time it frees the good student to progress at *his* rate without being impeded by his slower classmates. If it could be so advantageous to those at both ends of the learning spectrum, how useful it could be to the greater body of students in the middle.

At the secondary school level, mathematics could become an experimental science, enabling a student to go from the linear and quadratic equation to those of higher powers. These slim, pocket-size calculators could themselves provide the necessary degree of motivation.

The hand-held calculator is surely one of the most interesting fruits of computer technology—it has made instant solutions available for everyone rather than only for the military and those in higher education and on the institutional level. It may be freely purchased in the friendly neighborhood discount store. It is *here* and *now*.

10

THE FUTURE POCKET CALCULATOR

Despite the burgeoning sales of the modern hand-held calculator, it will probably change in several respects. It is bound to come down in price even more than it has. It is destined to be one of the more popular household items and will probably replace the proverbial fountain pen as a Confirmation or Bar Mitzvah gift.

Even though the technology exists to micro-miniaturize the calculator far more than it is already, this will not be done because people cannot accurately enter the figures for a calculation if the buttons are too small. Nor will they be able to read the result accurately if the display is too tiny. As it is, one severe criticism of the modern mini-calculator is that it is so easy to enter the wrong data. What is needed is a better "input" system that will, if not eliminate the possibility of entering the wrong numbers entirely, at least minimize it.

Something that none of the calculator manufacturers seems to have considered is the need that so many of us have to simply count. The electronic circuitry already in the calculator is surely capable of only a minor change so that the user, starting from any arbitrary number, could just press a *single* button and advance the counter by 1. It is true that we can always add 1 by pressing two buttons, but that is twice as much work as it should be. It can be circumvented by resorting to the following technique, but this really shouldn't be necessary. Here is the technique for use on the medium-priced calculator.

With the calculator in constant mode, key in a number starting with 1, filling up the rest of the display with zeros. Now press the multiplication button. Enter the number 1, followed by a string of zeros terminated by the number 1.

Typically, we would be multiplying together

$$10000000. \times 1.0000001$$

The result of this multiplication is

$$10000001.$$

Each time the [=] key is pressed the product will increase by 1 in the farthest right digits of the number in the display. This part of the number can therefore be used as a counter, requiring only the pressing of one button—the equal sign. Note that counting begins with 1 and not zero.

Should counting be required to start from a number greater than 1, the large number keyed in first should end with that number minus 1.

The pocket calculator of the future should be constructed so that it should be able to print out clearly certain results at the discretion of the user. Those calculators that currently have such a printing device are not only expensive and bulky, but also use reels of heat-sensitive paper that often lack the clarity one would associate with a precision instrument.

When calculating a long series of results it is sometimes desirable to plot them so that one can see the resulting graph. Of course, it would be nice to be able to make a hard copy of such a graph.

As one becomes adept at the use of a pocket calculator one develops techniques or approaches of one's own. These techniques could possibly be extremely useful to thousands of other people and such information should be readily available to them all. In order to disseminate such knowledge a nonprofit organization should be formed covering the international community. Perhaps it should be called QUICK, an acronym for "Questions of Universal Interest in Calculator Know-how." The author offers himself as the organizer should there be a demand for it on the part of the general public.

The organization should receive suggestions, complaints and criticisms from calculator users the world over, and should publish a bulletin. For a minimum fee each subscriber would be regularly entitled to the latest bulletin of information. Such a scheme would be of value to all users and would act as a kind of advisory board to the calculator manufacturers.

Finally, it is most desirable to have a hand-held calculator capable of storing a series of, say, up to 100 instructions (certainly 10, at least) so that the calculator becomes "programable." This means that in addition to its ability to calculate, it should be much like a modern computer—the so-called "electronic brain"—in that it should be able to execute a *series* of instructions automatically, if necessary, changing the contents of the instructions. The technology to do this is already at hand and the sales of such programable calculators could reach astronomic proportions.

Since this book first went to press a programmable pocket calculator has indeed appeared on the market. It is called the HP-65 and retails at $800. The HP-65 represents a quantum jump in progress in the pocket calculator field. No bigger in size than a pack of cigarettes, this little giant of a calculator is capable of all the calculation ability of its older brother and sister, the HP-35 and

HP-45. In addition, it can be programmed to execute the instructions fed to it by an inserted magnetic tape the size of a stick of chewing gum. It is difficult to foresee what the rest of the calculator industry is going to do to compete with the HP-65. It seems fairly certain, however, that there will be no competitor around for at least three years, even though, as itemized in the survey of pocket calculators found in this book, several companies have already produced excellent calculators with advanced features which compare most favorably with the HP-35.

As an ordinary calculator the HP-65 is an extremely powerful scientific calculator, providing no less than 51 separate preprogrammed functions operated directly from the keyboard. To take advantage of one of the prerecorded program packages available with the HP-65, all one has to do is insert it. The packages refer to specific disciplines like surveying, mathematics, statistics, electrical engineering, and medicine. A library of HP-65 programs is available to all users. These programs are listed in catalogs and are circulated periodically to subscribing owners.

In recent years computer programming has become an integral part of almost every college program, and in New York City alone there are already more than fifty high schools where computer programming is taught on an official basis. This trend is bound to spread all over the country, not only to almost all high schools, but into the elementary schools as well.

If in 1973 there were fifty high schools teaching computer programming and this number increases by 5.16% each year, how many schools will be teaching computer programming by 1980?

Where's the pocket calculator . . . ?

APPENDICES

APPENDIX A

OVERFLOW AND UNDERFLOW

CALCULATION OVERFLOW

If one were to multiply together two 8-digit integers, say

12345678 and 12345678

on the typical medium-priced 8-digit pocket calculator, one would not be surprised to find that the result is impossible to fit into the display. The result is actually a 15-digit number, which on the HP-35 is immediately converted to its scientific-notation value of $1.524157653 \times 10^{14}$.

Many calculators will inform the user that the result of such a calculation is too big to be displayed, by means of an indicator. This indicator is usually referred to as an *overflow indicator* since the result "flows over" or "overflows" the capacity of the machine. This may have the effect of locking the calculator, which then can be used only after it has been cleared. Division of a number by zero—since it is not defined mathematically—also will usually set the overflow indicator.

If the result of a calculation sets the overflow indicator, one can arrive at an estimate of the true answer by moving the decimal point eight places to the right. It should be realized that only the first eight digits are displayed.

The HP-35 indicates that overflow has occurred by displaying all 9's. Trying to take the tangent of 90° has this effect.

ENTRY OVERFLOW

Trying to key in a number that contains more digits than the display can handle will, on some calculators, set another overflow indicator. This is called entry overflow.

UNDERFLOW

Multiplying together two small numbers such as

$$.0000001 \times .0000001$$

will yield a very small product. The answer actually, as shown on the HP-35 is 1×10^{-14}. This number is too small to be displayed on the typical medium-priced calculator. Such a situation is spoken of as "underflow." Some calculators alert the user to the occurrence of underflow by setting an underflow indicator, while others are designed to treat such results as zero, which is, in fact, displayed.

APPENDIX B

ADVANCED TECHNIQUES FOR THE MEDIUM-PRICED CALCULATOR

To satisfy the needs and curiosity of the more sophisticated reader we are including here some advanced techniques. Because the inexpensive calculator does not have provision for a decimal point or a constant, all of the techniques we shall describe are not suited to it. The expensive calculator, on the other hand, has most of the functions to be described here readily available at the touch of a button. It follows therefore that this chapter will be devoted to the medium-priced calculator with a constant feature, floating decimal and the four standard functions of addition, subtraction, multiplication and division. In each of the following examples utilizing the constant feature, it is assumed that the second number of a multiplication is treated as a constant multiplier.

1 | ADVANCED COUNTING TECHNIQUES

As the reader will recall, we have already shown how one can count on the pocket calculator by pressing one button only. With the calculator in constant mode the number 10,000,000 was keyed in and multiplied by the number 1.0000001. The pressing of the [=] button advanced the farthest right digit by 1 each time it was pressed.

Furthermore, we pointed out that one can initialize the counter to any desired number by incorporating that number minus 1 into the first number keyed in, as in the following example, where we want to initialize the counter to 97. In constant mode:

$$10000096 \times 1.0000001$$

The first time the [=] button is pressed, 97 appears at the extreme right of the display, and for each subsequent press of the [=] button the counter advances by one.

Suppose now that we wish to count by a number other than one; for example, by an increment of two. This increment is entered as the left-hand part of the first number keyed in, as in the following example, where it is desired to count by two. In constant mode:

$$20000000 \times 1.0000001$$

The first time the [=] button is pressed the display will register a 2 in the rightmost position. Each subsequent touch of the [=] button will increase the number in the display by two.

As a third example we now show how to count by 3 beginning with the number 17 in the display. (From now on, a *K* will indicate "change to constant mode," and *CHN* will mean "change to chain mode.")

In order that the first time the [=] button is pressed the display shows the number 17, we must enter 17 minus the increment (in this case 3) giving 14, as shown:

$$K \quad 30000014 \times 1.0000001$$

Each time the [=] button is pressed, the number at

the extreme right of the display will increase in steps of 3, beginning with the number 17.

2 | ADVANCED TECHNIQUES USING THE CONSTANT SWITCH

Basically there are five principles that should be clearly understood in order to fully exploit the constant feature of the pocket calculator. They are:

(1) How to exit from constant mode
(2) How to divide *into* a number instead of *by* a number
(3) How to raise a number to a high power
(4) Changing the value of the constant while in constant mode
(5) Making a late exit from constant mode

A | Exiting from Constant Mode

Consider the following:

$$2^5 + 3$$

To calculate 2^5 all we need do is:

K 2 [×] [=] [=] [=] [=]

The result of 32 will appear in the display. However, following this sequence of operations with

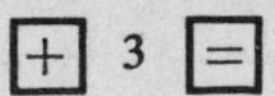

will *not* give the correct result, but rather will display a 6, which comes from multiplying 3 by 2. This happens because the number 2 is still in effect as a constant multiplier. What is needed at this point is a way of getting out of constant mode. Simply switching from constant mode to chain mode after 2^5 is calculated is insufficient and gives the same incorrect result. The reason for this is that when the calculator is switched out of constant mode it is still set up for one last constant operation. The way to overcome this problem is to carry out the following sequence of operations:

K 2 [×] [=] [=] [=] *CHN* [=] [+] 3 [=]

B | Dividing into a Number

Consider the following:

$$\frac{4}{2+3}$$

The reader should disregard the fact that the example shown involves numbers of one digit only. Our purpose is to explain how such a problem may be solved *in general* in an efficient manner. What we mean by "efficient" is that the number of steps involved should be minimal and minimal use made of a scratch pad.

The above expression can be evaluated using the following sequence:

1	**2**	**3**	**4**	**5**	**6**	**7**	**8**
2	[+]	3	*K*	[÷]	[=]	4	[=]

which does not necessitate the use of a scratch pad at all. What this does is first to add 2 to 3. Constant mode is then entered and the number is divided by itself in the next two steps, entering the sum, 5, as the constant divisor. The sequence 4 [=] gives the result 4÷5=.8.

C | Raising a Number to a Power

It should be pointed out that when raising a number to a power, that power must always be an integer power. (This is not true of the higher-priced pocket calculators where provision is, in fact, made to raise numbers to any power.)

We have already shown how expressions like

$$3^5 \text{ and } 2^7$$

may be evaluated efficiently. We would now like to discuss problems of the following two types:

$$(2^3)^5 \text{ and } (1.1)^{100}$$

The first-mentioned expression could be tackled as follows:

1	2	3	4	5	6	7	8	9	10	11	12
2	*K*	[×]	[=]	*CHN*	[=]	[×]	*K*	[=]	[=]	[=]	[=]

The number 2 is cubed in the way already described, leaving the constant mode before the [=] is pressed the second time. The number 8 is now in the display—this is 2^3. This number now has to be raised to the fifth power. This may be done in the ordinary way. (The scheme will also work with steps 5 and 8 omitted.)

The second expression

$$(1.1)^{100}$$

can be calculated using the following sequence:

1.1 *K* [×] (followed by the [=] button hit 99 times in succession).

This, however, is hardly an acceptable method; it is error-prone, tedious and time-consuming.

In order to handle this problem efficiently one may resort to *prime factors.*

The prime factors of 100 are

2,2,5,5

The problem can now be solved by converting the original expression to its equivalent form as shown below:

$$(1.1)^{100} = ((((1.1)^2)^2)^5)^5$$

This may be done as follows:

1	2	3	4	5	6	7	8	9	10
1.1	☒	⊟	☒	⊟	☒	*K*	⊟	⊟	⊟
11	12	13	14	15	16	17	18		
CHN	⊟	☒	*K*	⊟	⊟	⊟	⊟		

Raising a number to a negative power is the same as raising that number to the positive power and then finding its reciprocal. For example,

$$3^{-5} = \frac{1}{3^5}$$

The expression $\frac{1}{3^5}$ can be converted into two other equivalent forms, each of which leads to a different method of calculation:

$$\frac{1}{3^5} = \left(\frac{1}{3}\right)^5 = \cfrac{\cfrac{\cfrac{\cfrac{\cfrac{1}{3}}{3}}{3}}{3}}{3}$$

The expression $\frac{1}{3^5}$ can be evaluated by the following sequence of operations:

1	2	3	4	5	6	7	8	9	10	11	12
3	*K*	☒	⊟	⊟	⊟	*CHN*	⊟	*K*	⊞÷	⊟	⊟

The expression $\left(\frac{1}{3}\right)^5$ can be calculated as follows

1	2	3	4	5	6	7	8	9
1	÷	3	*K*	×	=	=	=	=

Last, the expression

$$\cfrac{\cfrac{\cfrac{\cfrac{\cfrac{1}{3}}{3}}{3}}{3}}{3}$$

is found by the following sequence:

1	2	3	4	5	6	7	8	9
1	÷	3	*K*	=	=	=	=	=

D | Changing the Value of the Constant While in Constant Mode

Consider the following sequence of operations:

K 2 × 3 ÷ 4 =

What would you expect the final constant to be? Let us go through this sequence step by step.

When 2 is multiplied by 3 in constant mode, 3 is the constant multiplier and the result 6 is displayed. After dividing by 4 the result is 1.5. The question now raised concerns the value of the constant. Is it × 3 or is it ÷ 4? The latter is the correct answer. In fact this is precisely the way a constant may be changed during a calculation.

As an illustration of this procedure, consider the expression

$$((1.2)^3)^4$$

which can be evaluated by the following steps:

1.2 *K* [×] [=] [=] [×] [=] [=] [=]

E | Making a Late Exit from Constant Mode

Assume we are in the process of calculating an expression like

$$(1.11)^7 + 5$$

In raising 1.11 to the 7th power we realize that we have inadvertently gone through the following steps:

K 1.11 [×] [=] [=] [=] [=] [=] [=]

rather than:

K 1.11 [×] [=] [=] [=] [=] [=] *CHN* [=]

The first situation may be corrected by following it with

[×] 1 *CHN* [+] 5 [=]

3 | REWRITING EQUATIONS FOR CONVENIENCE

It is often necessary to rewrite an equation so that it can be handled more conveniently by the pocket calculator. Consider the following task:

$$(2\times3) + (4\times5)$$

A little thought will indicate that this calculation cannot be performed directly without writing down an intermediate result. However, by rewriting the expression we get the following:

$$\left(\frac{2\times3}{5}+4\right)\times5$$

which may be handled on the pocket calculator as follows without the need to write down anything:

2 [×] 3 [÷] 5 [+] 4 [×] 5 [=]

In general,

$$(A \times B) + (C \times D)$$

may be reformulated as:

$$\left(\frac{A \times B}{D} + C\right) D$$

The reader is alerted to the fact that many other expressions are capable of reformulations such that they lend themselves to easier solution on the pocket calculator.

4 | TRUNCATING AND ROUNDING

TRUNCATING

When a number is truncated it loses its fractional portion. Thus the number 5.678 becomes equal to 5 when it is truncated. Similarly, 2.999 becomes 2 when truncated and 3 remains 3 when truncated.

It is sometimes convenient to replace a number in the display by its truncated value. This may be done directly by the following method, regardless of what number is in the display. In fact, one need not even look at the display.

[÷] 10000000 [×] 10000000 [=]

Try it—you'll find that it works beautifully.

ROUNDING

The fraction ⅓ expressed as a decimal number is

.3333333

Rounded to two decimal places, it becomes .33. Also, the fraction ⅔ expressed as a decimal number is

.6666666

which, rounded to two decimal places, becomes .67.

Some calculators provide automatic rounding features. For the benefit of those with calculators *not* having these rounding features (and they are in the majority), there is a method to round a number in the display to any desired number of decimal places.

To round to the nearest whole number, simply add .5 and perform the truncating procedure described above.

For rounding from 1 to 6 decimal places, refer to the chart below.

No. of Places	Operations		
1	+ .05	÷ 1000000	× 1000000
2	+ .005	÷ 100000	× 100000
3	+ .0005	÷ 10000	× 10000
4	+ .00005	÷ 1000	× 1000
5	+ .000005	÷ 100	× 100
6	+ .0000005	÷ 10	× 10

5 | GENERATING RANDOM NUMBERS

To solve a certain group of problems such as game simulation, it is necessary to have access to random numbers. These may be read off a table of random numbers or may be generated by the calculator owner himself.

On some inexpensive calculators the following procedure can be adopted. Enter a number that fills up the entire display. The [×] button is then pressed. Each time it is pressed a new random number is generated. Either the entire number may be regarded as the random number or any particular digit or combination of digits.

On the medium-priced calculator the above procedure will not work as a rule. Instead one may resort to the following scheme:

A number close to 1 and ending in an odd digit, e.g., 1.0000173, is keyed in, followed by the sequence:

[×] *K* [=] [=] . . .

Each time the [=] button is pressed a new random number is generated.

6 | AN ADVANCED METHOD FOR FINDING SQUARE ROOTS

There are many methods for finding square roots. One of them, the Newton-Raphson method, has already been described in detail.

The method we shall now describe—the Lewis method—differs from the others in that no scratch pad is needed, for no intermediate results have to be written down. The method works best for relatively small numbers. First divide the number by a perfect square and at the end multiply the result by the square root of that perfect square. Preferably the perfect square should be the closest square below the number whose square root is needed.

Suppose, for example, that we wish to calculate the

square root of 99. The closest perfect square below 99 is 9^2 which is 81. Dividing 99 by 81 gives 1.2222222.

We then find the square root of 1.2222222 which is close to 1. This square root is multiplied by 9 giving the square root of 99. The mathematics behind this is:

$$\sqrt{99} = \sqrt{81 \times 1.2222222} = 9 \times \sqrt{1.2222222}$$

THE LEWIS METHOD

N is the number that resulted from dividing the original number by a perfect square. In the case cited above *N* would be equal to 1.2222222.

Let $n = N - 1$. In this case *n* would be equal to 0.2222222.

Now the following sequence of operations should be carried out:

1	2	3	4	5	6	7	8	9
2	[=]	*K*	[÷]	[=]	*CHN*	[enter *n*]	[=]	[+]

Observe the number in the display. Repeat steps 1 through 9. Again observe the display. If it changes from the previous observation, repeat the sequence again. After several times around, the number in the display after step 9 will not be different from the last observation. As this point enter the following final sequence:

1	2	3	4
1	[×]	[square root of perfect square]	[=]

The result in the display will be the square root of the original number.

In order to familiarize the reader with this seemingly complex procedure we shall describe in detail an actual example. Let us find the square root of 35.

The closest square under 35 is 25 which is 5^2. We therefore key in 35 and divide by 25. This gives a result of 1.4:

$$\sqrt{35} = \sqrt{25 \times 1.4} = 5\sqrt{1.4}$$

What we now need to find is the square root of 1.4. This number, 1.4, is the value N defined above.

$$n = N - 1 = 0.4$$

Here is the schematic:

Sequence	1	2	3	4
Operation	2	[=]	*K*	[÷]
Display	2.	2.	2.	2.

Sequence	5	6	7	8
Operation	[=]	*CHN*	.4	[=]
Display	1.	1.	.4	.2

Sequence	9	10	11	12
Operation	[+]	2	[=]	*K*
Display	.2	2.	2.2	2.2

Sequence	13	14	15	16
Operation	[÷]	[=]	*CHN*	.4
Display	2.2	1.	1.	.4

Sequence	17	18	19	20
Operation	[=]	[+]	2	[=]
Display	.1818181	.1818181	2.	2.1818181

Sequence	21	22	23	24
Operation	*K*	[÷]	[=]	*CHN*
Display	2.1818181	2.1818181	1.	1.

Sequence	25	26	27	28
Operation	.4	[=]	[+]	2
Display	.4	.1833333	.1833333	2.

Sequence	29	30	31	32
Operation	[=]	*K*	[÷]	[=]
Display	2.1833333	2.1833333	2.1833333	1.

Sequence	33	34	35	36
Operation	*CHN*	.4	[=]	[+]
Display	1.	.4	.1832061	.1832061

Sequence	37	38	39	40
Operation	2	[=]	*K*	[÷]
Display	2.	2.1832061	2.1832001	2.1832001

Sequence	41	42	43	44
Operation	[=]	*CHN*	.4	[=]
Display	1.	1.	.4	.1832167

Sequence	45	46	47	48
Operation	[+]	2	[=]	*K*
Display	.1832167	2.	2.1832167	2.1832167

Sequence	49	50	51	52
Operation	[÷]	[=]	*CHN*	.4
Display	2.1832167	1.	1.	.4

Sequence	53	54	55	56
Operation	[=]	[+]	2	[=]
Display	.1832158	.1832158	2.	2.1832158

Sequence	57	58	59	60
Operation	*K*	[÷]	[=]	*CHN*
Display	2.1832158	2.1832158	1.	1.

Sequence	61	62	63	64
Operation	.4	[=]	[+]	2
Display	.4	.1832159	.1832159	2.

Sequence	65	66	67	68
Operation	[=]	*K*	[÷]	[=]
Display	2.1832159	2.1832159	2.1832159	1.

Sequence	69	70	71	72
Operation	*CHN*	.4	[=]	[+]
Display	1.	.4	.1832159	.1832159

Note that the display in steps 63 and 72 is identical, which means that we now enter the final sequence of steps:

Sequence	73	74	75	76
Operation	1	[×]	5	[=]
Display	1.	1.1832159	5.	5.9160795

The number in the display, 5.9160795, is the square root of 35.

APPENDIX C

A SURVEY OF POCKET CALCULATORS LISTED IN ALPHABETICAL ORDER OF MODEL NAME

The list that follows is far from exhaustive. It will no doubt be out of date by the time this book appears. The prices listed will most likely change in favor of the consumer. New calculators are coming on the market with ever-increasing speed and variety.

The best approach for a prospective owner is to decide what features he wants and to shop various stores for the best buy.

ABATRON 800

Peripheral Magnetics Corp.
Los Angeles, Calif.

DIMENSIONS	6⅛ × 3½ × 1⅜ inches
WEIGHT	10¼ ounces
BATTERIES	6 AA, life of 10¼ hours; battery level indicator
CHARACTERISTICS	wide viewing angle; 8-digit display; preset or floating decimal; overflow indicator; constant switch; clear-entry key; has a change-sign key; rounds off decimals
PRICE	$100

BOWMAR MX20

Bowmar ALI Inc.
531 Main St.
Acton, Mass. 01720

DIMENSIONS	2¾ × 6 × ¾ inches
WEIGHT	6 ounces
BATTERIES	3 AA disposable batteries
CHARACTERISTICS	floating decimal; four functions; constant operable in each function
PRICE	$60

Note: Also available are the following: Bowmar MX 40, $80; Bowmar MX 50, $90; Bowmar MX 61, with %, $90; Bowmar MX 70, with memory, $65; Bowmar MX 75, with memory and %, $80; Bowmar MX 80, with 10 digits and %, $75; and Bowmar MX 100, with trigonometric functions, $140.

BUSICOM HANDY LE 100A

Busicom Corp.
31 East 28th St.,
New York, N.Y. 10016

DIMENSIONS	2.57 × 4.79 × 0.89 inches
WEIGHT	7 ounces
BATTERIES	4 dry cells, life of 10 hours; battery level indicator
CHARACTERISTICS	10-digit display; underflow and overflow indicator; round-off; decimal point selector; floating and fixed decimal; clear-entry key; constant switch
PRICE	about $125

Note: The same company produces a Personal 60-DA that has 6-digit display with double length projection. In addition, it has an adjustable fixed decimal. It sells for $80. The company also has an LE-80A that is supposedly the smallest calculator available (4 oz.; 2½ × 4¾ × ¾). Several other models are available.

CASIO-MINI

Casio, Inc.
Suite 14011, 1 World Trade Center
New York, N.Y. 10048

DIMENSIONS	5⅝ × 2⅞ × 1½ inches
WEIGHT	11 ounces
BATTERIES	4 AA, life 14 hours
CHARACTERISTICS	6-digit display (double length projection) with blue-green color; fixed decimal point; very wide viewing angle; display digits are ¼ inch high
PRICE	$35

Note: An all new Casio-Mini calculator has recently been advertised. It provides zero suppression and a switch for fixed 2-point decimal or none at all. It is 6 × 3¼ × 1¼ inches, weighs 11 ounces, and is priced at $40. This company has recently announced 3 other types of calculators: Casio 8E features 8-digit display, floating decimal, constant for × and ÷ with optional AC adaptor, price $60. Casio Root-8 features floating decimal, constant for × and ÷, and square root, price $80. Casio Root-8S with large display, square root, reciprocal, constant for × and ÷, and automatic overflow check, price $75.

COLUMBIA

Columbia Scientific
Santa Monica, Calif.

DIMENSIONS	5¼ × 3 × 1½ inches
WEIGHT	9¾ ounces
BATTERIES	6 AA, life of 26 hours
CHARACTERISTICS	guide bump on "5" key for orientation purposes; full floating decimal; 8-red-digit display; constant switch; clear-entry key; overflow indicator
PRICE	$100

Note: Other, more expensive models are available.

COLUMBIA II

RBM—Titan Corp.
P.O. Box 1246
Havre, Mont. 59501

DIMENSIONS	3 × 5-9/16 × ⅞ inches
WEIGHT	7 ounces
BATTERIES	built-in rechargeable
CHARACTERISTICS	full floating decimal; 8-digit display; clear-entry key; constant switch; comes in impact-resistant carrying-case; overflow indicator
PRICE	$75

Note: The same company now produces three other models. Columbia I operates on 5 penlight batteries and shuts off automatically in 15 seconds. Weighs 11 ounces, floating decimal, constant for multiplication and division, 8-digit display, sells for $60. Columbia III has rechargeable batteries, AC adapter/charger, percentage key, automatic constant for multiplication and division, and floating and/or fixed decimal. Weighs 6 ounces and sells for $85. Columbia Memory III is similar to Columbia III but has discount/add-on memory system. Sells for $100.

COMMODORE MINUTEMAN 2

Commodore Business Machines, Inc.
390 Reed St.
Santa Clara, Calif. 95050

DIMENSIONS	6 × 3½ × 1¾ inches
WEIGHT	13 ounces
BATTERIES	built-in, life 3 hours; recharge time 14 hours
CHARACTERISTICS	guide bump in "5" key for orientation; full floating decimal; clear-entry key; overflow indicator; 8-digit display; constant switch
PRICE	$90

Note: Also available is the Commodore MM-3, as small as a pack of cigarettes (2¾ × 4 × 1 inches). It weighs 6 ounces and sells for $44, including AC adaptor. In addition, this company produces the Commodore 8-digit minicalculator with memory and % key. Sells for $88. The Commodore 2-SR has four functions, square root, inverse, square, %, memory and sells for $100. Finally, there is the Commodore 3-S, with square and square root keys, floating decimal, reverse sign key, and rechargeable kit included, at $60.

COMMODORE US-4

Commodore Business Machines, Inc.
390 Reed St.
Santa Clara, Calif. 95050

DIMENSIONS	1½ × 3¼ × 5½ inches
WEIGHT	10 ounces
BATTERIES	disposable penlight batteries and AC
CHARACTERISTICS	8-digit bluish-green ¼″ display; has a memory location plus enter and recall keys; dual-function Clear key—pressing once clears entry and redisplays previous result, pressing the second time clears the machine with the exception of the memory; algebraic logic; full floating decimal; constant key
PRICE	$90

CRAIG 4501 A

Craig Corp.
921 W. Artesia Blvd.
Compton, Calif. 90220

DIMENSIONS	5¼ × 3 × 1½ inches
WEIGHT	10½ ounces
BATTERIES	built-in, rechargeable, life of 10½ hours; battery level indicator; recharge time 14 hours
CHARACTERISTICS	guide bump on "5" key for orientation; full floating decimal; 8-digit display; overflow indicator; constant switch; clear-entry key; wide viewing angle
PRICE	$150

DATAKING MODEL 868

Unitrex of America Inc.
350 Fifth Ave.
New York, N.Y. 10001

DIMENSIONS	5¼ × 2¾ × 1¼ inches
WEIGHT	8 ounces
BATTERIES	disposable penlight batteries or adapter and rechargeable batteries
CHARACTERISTICS	8-digit LED display; floating decimal and optional 2-digit fixed point; percentage button
PRICE	$100

Note: The same company also produces a model 848 for $90.

ELDORADO TOUCHMAGIC

Eldorado Electrodata Corp.
935 Detroit Ave.
Concord, Calif. 94518

DIMENSIONS	3½ × 6½ × 1½ inches
WEIGHT	16 ounces
BATTERIES	rechargeable built-in battery
CHARACTERISTICS	large 8-digit display; floating decimal; overflow indicator
PRICE	$90

Note: The same company produces a more expensive model, the Mathmagic B, that has a constant switch, a clear-entry switch and AC/DC operation.

HEWLETT PACKARD HP-35

Hewlett Packard Advanced Products
10900 Wolfe Rd.
Cupertino, Calif. 95014

DIMENSIONS	5.8 × 3.2 × (.7 to 1.3) inches
WEIGHT	9 ounces
BATTERIES	rechargeable built-in battery; life 3–5 hours; recharge time 14 hours; battery level indicator
CHARACTERISTICS	10-digit and 2-digit-exponent in display; has the following keys: π, x^y, 1/x, $\log_{10}$, $\log_e$, e^x, sin x, cos x, tan x, arc sin x, arc cos x, arc tan x, $\sqrt{x}$, change sign, clear-entry; 4-register stack; storage location; when necessary, converts to scientific notation; full floating point
PRICE	$300

Note: This company also produces an advanced scientific calculator, the HP-45, that sells for $400. It performs many additional functions. The HP-80 is the specialized business calculator that also sells for $400. Recently the company has announced a *programmable* version of the HP-35 and HP-45. Magnetic tape cards are inserted into this match-box sized calculator-cum-computer. Called the HP-65 or "Superstar," it sells for $800.

I.C.P. 525

International Consumer Products Ltd.
350 Fifth Avenue
New York, N.Y. 10001

DIMENSIONS	5⅝ × 3¼ × 1¼ inches
WEIGHT	8 ounces

BATTERIES	4 AA disposable batteries
CHARACTERISTICS	memory; 8-digit display; floating decimal; %; constant key
PRICE	$80

Note: This company also produces a Model ICP 530 with memory, %, automatic constant in all functions, 8-digit, full floating decimal. Sells for $80. The same company has recently produced a new mini-scientific calculator called the ICP 537. In addition to the four basic functions it has sine, cosine, tangent, log (both bases), square roots, inverse functions, and memory. Retails for $160.

I J I MINI A

Iain Jones International, Ltd.
6428 N.E. Expressway
Norcross, Ga. 30071

DIMENSIONS	5⅞ × 3⅛ × 1 inches
WEIGHT	7¼ ounces
BATTERIES	1 9-volt rechargeable battery, life of 1 hour; battery level indicator; recharge time 14 hours
CHARACTERISTICS	full floating decimal; 8-digit display; overflow indicator; constant switch; clear-entry key
PRICE	$90

Note: This company has also model Phoenix/B, with full floating decimal; rechargeable nickel-cadmium batteries; a constant feature for multiplication and division.

KEYSTONE 350

Berkey Photo Inc.
2 Keystone Pl.
Paramus, N.J.

DIMENSIONS	5½ × 3-1/5 × 1¾ inches
WEIGHT	9½ ounces
BATTERIES	4 AA or AC
CHARACTERISTICS	8-digit display; 16-digit calculation; % key; full floating or two-place fixed decimal; constant key for +, −, ÷, ×, and %
PRICE	$70

Note: Also available are Keystone 370 with %, at $75; Keystone 390 with %, and memory, at $95; and Keystone 395 with memory, square root, reciprocal, and squares, at $105.

LLOYD'S E681 ACCUMATIC 200

Lloyd's Electronics Inc.
G.P.O. Box 367
East Paterson, N.J. 07407

DIMENSIONS	5.7 × 3.2 × 1.1 inches
WEIGHT	10 ounces
BATTERIES	AC/DC, 4 penlight or nicad rechargeable batteries
CHARACTERISTICS	8-digit floating or fixed decimal; overflow indicator, clear-entry key; % key
PRICE	$100

MELCOR 360B

Melcor Electronics
1750 New Highway
Farmingdale, N.Y. 11735

DIMENSIONS	5.9 × 3 × .8 inches
WEIGHT	6½ ounces
BATTERIES	9-volt alkaline battery, life 10 hours; AC adapter
CHARACTERISTICS	8-digit full floating decimal; 3 storage registers; automatic round-off; constant feature
PRICE	$100

Note: Also available in a Model 360R that recharges in 4 hours, also selling for $100.

MELCOR 380

Melcor Electronics
1750 New Highway
Farmingdale, N.Y. 11735

DIMENSIONS	6 × 3 × 7⅛ inches
WEIGHT	10 ounces
BATTERIES	disposable 9V battery or AC
CHARACTERISTICS	8-digit display; floating decimal point; has % key; has a memory location for extra storage; clear-entry key
PRICE	$80

Note: The same company produces both a cheaper and a more expensive model: Melcor 1000, with four functions, selling for $50; and Melcor 400, a scientific model with memory, square root, square and reciprocal features. Comes with AC adapter and sells for $100 or less at discount houses.

MIIDA 8

Miida Electronics
2 Hammarskjold Plaza
New York, N.Y. 10017

DIMENSIONS	5½ × 3⅞ × 1 inches
WEIGHT	11 ounces
BATTERIES	AC/mini-nicad rechargeable batteries, life of 4½ hours
CHARACTERISTICS	8-digit display; constant key; full floating decimal
PRICE	$110

PANASONIC 860

Panasonic
200 Park Ave.
New York, N.Y. 10017

DIMENSIONS	4 × 6½ × 1¾ inches
WEIGHT	18 ounces
BATTERIES	AC or 4 AA
CHARACTERISTICS	large 8-digit greenish display; constant switch; full floating decimal; has π key; has $\sqrt{\ }$ key
PRICE	$150

Note: Panasonic also makes the 850 model that sells for $140 but does not have the π or $\sqrt{\ }$ keys. Also available is the Model 883 with 8-digit display, automatic rounding, and AC or batteries. Sells for $100.

PILOT 8

Goldsmith Brothers
77 Nassau St.
New York, N.Y. 10038

DIMENSIONS	3⅛ × 5⅝ × ⅞ inches
WEIGHT	information not available
BATTERIES	9-volt, life 4 hours, AC adapter included
CHARACTERISTICS	8-digit LED display; full floating decimal; constant key; algebraic logic
PRICE	$60

PIONEER I

Rapid Data Systems and Equipment, Ltd.
Rexdale, Ontario, Canada

DIMENSIONS	5⅜ × 3¼ × ⅞ inches
WEIGHT	6½ ounces
BATTERIES	1 9-volt battery, life of 5¾ hours; battery level indicator
CHARACTERISTICS	8-digit display; fixed 2-place floating decimal
PRICE	$60

POCKETRONIC

Canon U.S. Inc.
10 Nevada Drive
Lake Success, N.Y. 11040

Pocket printing calculator with charger.

PRICE	$117

Note: Also available is the Palmetronic LE-80M, which has a memory, battery check indicator and sells for $70.

RADIO SHACK EC 100

Radio Shack Co.
Fort Worth, Texas

DIMENSIONS	5¾ × 3½ × 1½ inches
WEIGHT	9¼ ounces
BATTERIES	4 AA, life of 18¼ hours; battery level indicator
CHARACTERISTICS	guide bump on "5" key for orientation; 8-digit display; overflow indicator; full floating decimal; clear-entry key; wide viewing angle
PRICE	$130

RAGEN MICRO-MINI

Ragen Precision Industries
9 Porele Ave.
North Arlington, N.J. 07032

DIMENSIONS	2⅜ × ⅞ × 3½ inches
WEIGHT	4 ounces
BATTERIES	miniature batteries
CHARACTERISTICS	8-digit liquid-crystal display; automatic round-off; overflow indicator; 16-digit entry
PRICE	$100

RAPIDMAN 800

Rapid Sales Corp.
29245 Stephenson Hwy.
Madison Heights, Mich. 48071

DIMENSIONS	5⅜ × 3¼ × ⅞ inches
WEIGHT	7½ ounces

BATTERIES	9-volt battery, and adapter for AC usage
CHARACTERISTICS	2-place decimal setting; 8-digit readout; storage register
PRICE	$50

Note: Also available is model 801, full floating point; uses nicad batteries; price $100.

REMINGTON 661

Sperry Rand
1290 Ave. of Americas
New York, N.Y.

DIMENSIONS	6 × 3.5 × 1.5 inches
WEIGHT	12 ounces
BATTERIES	4 AA, life 14 hours
CHARACTERISTICS	6-digit display (double length projection) with blue-green color; fixed decimal point; very wide viewing angle; display digits are ¼ inch high
PRICE	$50

SEARS CAT. 5885

Sears Roebuck

DIMENSIONS	5⅞ × 3 × 1⅜ inches
WEIGHT	7¼ ounces
BATTERIES	built-in, life of 2 hours; battery level indicator; recharge time 7 hours
CHARACTERISTICS	guide bump on "5" key for orientation; full floating decimal; 8-digit display; overflow indicator; constant switch; clear-entry key
PRICE	$99

SHARP ELSI MINI EL801

Sharp Electric Corp.
10 Keystone Pl.
Paramus, N.J. 07652

DIMENSIONS	2-15/16 × 1⅛ × 4 inches
WEIGHT	8 ounces
BATTERIES	4 dry cell AA, but various options are given; battery level indicator
CHARACTERISTICS	8-digit display; minus sign indicated to right of number; full floating point; constant key with constant mode indicator; automatically remembers first entry of a calculation
PRICE	$130

Note: The same company produces a model ELSI-8M that provides for a memory location, recall feature, and a 16-digit calculating facility.

SINCLAIR EXECUTIVE

Sinclair Radionics Ltd.
London Road
St. Ives
Huntington PE17 4HJ
England

DIMENSIONS	5 × 2 × ¼ inches [most compact]
WEIGHT	information not available
BATTERIES	information not available
CHARACTERISTICS	full floating decimal point; 8-digit red read-out; constant button; high intensity switch (which makes read-out brighter); algebraic logic; does not suppress trailing zeros
PRICE	$120

Note: This British company has recently produced a pocket scientific calculator with dimensions of 4.3 × 1.9 × 0.7 inches. It sells for about $115.

SUMMIT K 16

Summit International Corp.
Salt Lake City, Utah

DIMENSIONS	4 × 2¾ × 1⅜ inches
WEIGHT	8¼ ounces
BATTERIES	built-in rechargeable battery, life of 5 hours; battery level indicator; recharge time 3–4 hours
CHARACTERISTICS	guide bump on "5" key for orientation; 8-digit display; constant switch; clear-entry key; full floating decimal; has a change-sign key
PRICE	$70

Note: A cheaper model, K09V, is available for $80. Also a more expensive model, SQR16M, is available for $160. Latter has square root and a memory register. In addition, the company makes a Model MB-10 with 10 digits, 4 functions with constant, uses disposable batteries or AC, and weighs 2½ ounces. Sells for $109.

TEXAS INSTRUMENT DATAMATH TI 2500

Texas Instruments, Inc.
Dallas, Texas

DIMENSIONS	5⅜ × 3 × 1½ inches
WEIGHT	10½ ounces
BATTERIES	built-in, rechargeable, life of 8 hours; when battery is low it is indicated by decimal points appearing in display; recharge time 14–16 hours

CHARACTERISTICS	guide bump on "5" key for orientation; 8-digit display; full floating point; constant-entry switch; overflow and underflow indicators; on some units display fades after approximately 15 seconds to conserve life of battery; these units have CE/D button for displaying faded entry; has algebraic logic; shaded display
PRICE	$60

Note: Texas Instrument SR 10 is similar in many respects to the Datamath TI 2500 described above but contains some important additional features: $\sqrt{x}$ button for square root; x^2 button for squaring a number; 1/x button for reciprocals; +/− button for changing sign; and EE button for entering exponents. This calculator comes with an *Applications Guide* containing formulas to calculate all the trigonometric, logarithmic and other functions. Price $85. Surprisingly, this calculator, as sophisticated as it is, does not have a constant feature. It has automatic conversion to scientific notation on overflow; data may be entered in floating point, scientific notation, or any combination of the two. A calculator identical to the 2500 is now available but it runs on disposable batteries. Called the TI 2510, it sells for $48 at discount stores. Recently Texas Instrument announced a new model, the SR-50. It has many highly sophisticated features useful to the scientist, including squaring, finding the square root, factorial, hyperbolic functions, and degree to radian conversion. It sells for $170 but is obtainable for the time being only by direct mail.

UNICOM 103

Unicom Systems, Inc.
Rockwell Intl. Corp.
500 Fifth Ave., Suite 1010
New York, N.Y. 10036

DIMENSIONS	5¾ × 3 × ¾ inches
WEIGHT	6 ounces
BATTERIES	disposable 9-volt battery or rechargeable battery pack
CHARACTERISTICS	8-digit LED display; floating decimal; automatic constant for division and multiplication memory location
PRICE	$80

Note: The company also has a Model 102 which permits selection of full floating or fixed 0-7 place decimal setting and is priced at $60. It also produces the 202/SR and a 29-function calculator for scientists. It has trigonometric and log function, roots and powers, degree/radian selector, separate addressable memory, floating point, runs on disposable batteries, weighs 12 ounces, and sells for "under $200." Also manufactured by this company is the UNICOM 1000P Printing Calculator, which retails at $190.

UNISONIC MINI-CALCULATOR

Unisonic Corp.
16 W. 25 St.
New York, N.Y. 10010

DIMENSIONS	5⅝ × 2⅞ × 1½ inches
WEIGHT	11 ounces
BATTERIES	4 AA, life 14 hours
CHARACTERISTICS	6-digit display (double length projection) with blue-green color; fixed deci-

	mal point; very wide viewing angle; display digits are ¼ inch high
PRICE	$50

UNITREX MODEL 12H

Unitrex of America Inc.
350 Fifth Ave.
New York, N.Y. 10001

DIMENSIONS	5¾ × 2¾ × ¾ inches
WEIGHT	8 ounces
BATTERIES	2 cartridges—short- or long-term use; battery level indicator
CHARACTERISTICS	12-digit LED display; 0-, 2-, and 4-place fixed decimal; automatic display cutoff after 15 seconds
PRICE	$80

Note: Also available is an 8-digit calculator with constant, 0-4 decimal places, and AC-DC. Weighs 16 ounces, sells for $40.

APPENDIX D

TABLES OF RECIPROCALS AND SQUARE ROOTS

n	$\frac{1}{n}$	$\sqrt{n}$	n	$\frac{1}{n}$	$\sqrt{n}$
1	1,0000000	1,0000000	51	,0196078	7.1414284
2	,5000000	1.4142136	52	.0192308	7.2111026
3	,3333333	1.7320508	53	,0188679	7,2801099
4	,2500000	2,0000000	54	,0185185	7,3484692
5	,2000000	2,2360680	55	,0181818	7,4161985
6	,1666667	2,4494897	56	,0178571	7,4833148
7	,1428571	2,6457513	57	,0175439	7,5498344
8	,1250000	2,8284271	58	,0172414	7,6157731
9	,1111111	3,0000000	59	,0169492	7,6811457
10	,1000000	3,1622777	60	,0166667	7,7459667
11	,0909091	3.3166248	61	,0163934	7,8102497
12	,0833333	3.4641016	62	,0161290	7,8740079
13	,0769231	3,6055513	63	,0158730	7,9372539
14	,0714286	3,7416574	64	,0156250	8,0000000
15	,0666667	3,8729833	65	,0153846	8,0622577
16	,0625000	4.0000000	66	,0151515	8,1240384
17	,0588235	4,1231056	67	,0149254	8,1853528
18	,0555556	4,2426407	68	,0147059	8,2462113
19	,0526316	4,3588989	69	,0144928	8,3066239
20	,0500000	4.4721360	70	,0142857	8,3666003
21	,0476190	4,5825757	71	,0140845	8,4261498
22	,0454545	4,6904158	72	,0138889	8,4852814
23	,0434783	4,7958315	73	,0136986	8,5440037
24	,0416667	4,8989795	74	,0135135	8,6023253
25	,0400000	5,0000000	75	,0133333	8,6602540
26	,0384615	5,0990195	76	,0131579	8,7177979
27	,0370370	5.1961524	77	,0129870	8.7749644
28	,0357143	5,2915026	78	,0128205	8,8317609
29	,0344828	5,3851648	79	,0126582	8.8881944
30	,0333333	5,4772256	80	,0125000	8,9442719
31	,0322581	5,5677644	81	,0123457	9,0000000
32	,0312500	5,6568542	82	,0121951	9,0553851
33	,0303030	5,7445626	83	,0120482	9,1104336
34	,0294118	5,8309519	84	,0119048	9,1651514
35	,0285714	5,9160798	85	,0117647	9,2195445
36	,0277778	6,0000000	86	,0116279	9,2736185
37	,0270270	6,0827625	87	,0114943	9,3273791
38	,0263158	6,1644140	88	,0113636	9.3808315
39	,0256410	6,2449980	89	,0112360	9,4339811
40	,0250000	6,3245553	90	,0111111	9,4868330
41	,0243902	6,4031242	91	,0109890	9,5393920
42	,0238095	6,4807407	92	,0108696	9,5916630
43	,0232558	6,5574385	93	,0107527	9,6436508
44	,0227273	6,6332496	94	,0106383	9,6953597
45	,0222222	6,7082039	95	,0105263	9,7467943
46	,0217391	6,7823300	96	,0104167	9,7979590
47	,0212766	6.8556546	97	,0103093	9,8488578
48	,0208333	6,9282032	98	,0102041	9,8994949
49	,0204082	7,0000000	99	,0101010	9,9498744
50	,0200000	7,0710678	100	,0100000	10.0000000

n	$\frac{1}{n}$	$\sqrt{n}$	n	$\frac{1}{n}$	$\sqrt{n}$
101	.0099010	10.0498756	151	.0066225	12.2882057
102	.0098039	10.0995049	152	.0065789	12.3288280
103	.0097087	10.1488916	153	.0065359	12.3693169
104	.0096154	10.1980390	154	.0064935	12.4096736
105	.0095238	10.2469508	155	.0064516	12.4498996
106	.0094340	10.2956301	156	.0064103	12.4899960
107	.0093458	10.3440804	157	.0063694	12.5299641
108	.0092593	10.3923048	158	.0063291	12.5698051
109	.0091743	10.4403065	159	.0062893	12.6095202
110	.0090909	10.4880885	160	.0062500	12.6491106
111	.0090090	10.5356538	161	.0062112	12.6885775
112	.0089286	10.5830052	162	.0061728	12.7279221
113	.0088496	10.6301458	163	.0061350	12.7671453
114	.0087719	10.6770783	164	.0060976	12.8062485
115	.0086957	10.7238053	165	.0060606	12.8452326
116	.0086207	10.7703296	166	.0060241	12.8840987
117	.0085470	10.8166538	167	.0059880	12.9228480
118	.0084746	10.8627805	168	.0059524	12.9614814
119	.0084034	10.9087121	169	.0059172	13.0000000
120	.0083333	10.9544512	170	.0058824	13.0384048
121	.0082645	11.0000000	171	.0058480	13.0766968
122	.0081967	11.0453610	172	.0058140	13.1148770
123	.0081301	11.0905365	173	.0057803	13.1529464
124	.0080645	11.1355287	174	.0057471	13.1909060
125	.0080000	11.1803399	175	.0057143	13.2287566
126	.0079365	11.2249722	176	.0056818	13.2664992
127	.0078740	11.2694277	177	.0056497	13.3041347
128	.0078125	11.3137085	178	.0056180	13.3416641
129	.0077519	11.3578167	179	.0055866	13.3790882
130	.0076923	11.4017543	180	.0055556	13.4164079
131	.0076336	11.4455231	181	.0055249	13.4536240
132	.0075758	11.4891253	182	.0054945	13.4907376
133	.0075188	11.5325626	183	.0054645	13.5277493
134	.0074627	11.5758369	184	.0054348	13.5646600
135	.0074074	11.6189500	185	.0054054	13.6014705
136	.0073529	11.6619038	186	.0053763	13.6381817
137	.0072993	11.7046999	187	.0053476	13.6747943
138	.0072464	11.7473401	188	.0053191	13.7113092
139	.0071942	11.7898261	189	.0052910	13.7477271
140	.0071429	11.8321596	190	.0052632	13.7840488
141	.0070922	11.8743421	191	.0052356	13.8202750
142	.0070423	11.9163753	192	.0052083	13.8564065
143	.0069930	11.9582607	193	.0051813	13.8924440
144	.0069444	12.0000000	194	.0051546	13.9283883
145	.0068966	12.0415946	195	.0051282	13.9642400
146	.0068493	12.0830460	196	.0051020	14.0000000
147	.0068027	12.1243557	197	.0050761	14.0356688
148	.0067568	12.1655251	198	.0050505	14.0712473
149	.0067114	12.2065556	199	.0050251	14.1067360
150	.0066667	12.2474487	200	.0050000	14.1421356

n	$\frac{1}{n}$	$\sqrt{n}$	n	$\frac{1}{n}$	$\sqrt{n}$
201	.0049751	14.1774469	251	.0039841	15.8429795
202	.0049505	14.2126704	252	.0039683	15.8745079
203	.0049261	14.2478068	253	.0039526	15.9059737
204	.0049020	14.2828569	254	.0039370	15.9373775
205	.0048780	14.3178211	255	.0039216	15.9687194
206	.0048544	14.3527001	256	.0039063	16.0000000
207	.0048309	14.3874946	257	.0038911	16.0312195
208	.0048077	14.4222051	258	.0038760	16.0623784
209	.0047847	14.4568323	259	.0038610	16.0934769
210	.0047619	14.4913767	260	.0038462	16.1245155
211	.0047393	14.5258390	261	.0038314	16.1554944
212	.0047170	14.5602198	262	.0038168	16.1864141
213	.0046948	14.5945195	263	.0038023	16.2172747
214	.0046729	14.6287388	264	.0037879	16.2480768
215	.0046512	14.6628783	265	.0037736	16.2788206
216	.0046296	14.6969385	266	.0037594	16.3095064
217	.0046083	14.7309199	267	.0037453	16.3401346
218	.0045872	14.7648231	268	.0037313	16.3707055
219	.0045662	14.7986486	269	.0037175	16.4012195
220	.0045455	14.8323970	270	.0037037	16.4316767
221	.0045249	14.8660687	271	.0036900	16.4620776
222	.0045045	14.8996644	272	.0036765	16.4924225
223	.0044843	14.9331845	273	.0036630	16.5227116
224	.0044643	14.9666295	274	.0036496	16.5529454
225	.0044444	15.0000000	275	.0036364	16.5831240
226	.0044248	15.0332964	276	.0036232	16.6132477
227	.0044053	15.0665192	277	.0036101	16.6433170
228	.0043860	15.0996689	278	.0035971	16.6733320
229	.0043668	15.1327460	279	.0035842	16.7032931
230	.0043478	15.1657509	280	.0035714	16.7332005
231	.0043290	15.1986842	281	.0035587	16.7630546
232	.0043103	15.2315462	282	.0035461	16.7928556
233	.0042918	15.2643375	283	.0035336	16.8226038
234	.0042735	15.2970585	284	.0035211	16.8522995
235	.0042553	15.3297097	285	.0035088	16.8819430
236	.0042373	15.3622915	286	.0034965	16.9115345
237	.0042194	15.3948043	287	.0034843	16.9410743
238	.0042017	15.4272486	288	.0034722	16.9705627
239	.0041841	15.4596248	289	.0034602	17.0000000
240	.0041667	15.4919334	290	.0034483	17.0293864
241	.0041494	15.5241747	291	.0034364	17.0587221
242	.0041322	15.5563492	292	.0034247	17.0880075
243	.0041152	15.5884573	293	.0034130	17.1172428
244	.0040984	15.6204994	294	.0034014	17.1464282
245	.0040816	15.6524758	295	.0033898	17.1755640
246	.0040650	15.6843871	296	.0033784	17.2046505
247	.0040486	15.7162336	297	.0033670	17.2336879
248	.0040323	15.7480157	298	.0033557	17.2626765
249	.0040161	15.7797338	299	.0033445	17.2916165
250	.0040000	15.8113883	300	.0033333	17.3205081

n	$\frac{1}{n}$	$\sqrt{n}$	n	$\frac{1}{n}$	$\sqrt{n}$
301	.0033223	17.3493516	351	.0028490	18.7349940
302	.0033113	17.3781472	352	.0028409	18.7616630
303	.0033003	17.4068952	353	.0028329	18.7882942
304	.0032895	17.4355958	354	.0028249	18.8148877
305	.0032787	17.4642492	355	.0028169	18.8414437
306	.0032680	17.4928557	356	.0028090	18.8679623
307	.0032573	17.5214155	357	.0028011	18.8944436
308	.0032468	17.5499288	358	.0027933	18.9208879
309	.0032362	17.5783958	359	.0027855	18.9472953
310	.0032258	17.6068169	360	.0027778	18.9736660
311	.0032154	17.6351921	361	.0027701	19.0000000
312	.0032051	17.6635217	362	.0027624	19.0262976
313	.0031949	17.6918060	363	.0027548	19.0525589
314	.0031847	17.7200451	364	.0027473	19.0787840
315	.0031746	17.7482393	365	.0027397	19.1049732
316	.0031646	17.7763888	366	.0027322	19.1311265
317	.0031546	17.8044938	367	.0027248	19.1572441
318	.0031447	17.8325545	368	.0027174	19.1833261
319	.0031348	17.8605711	369	.0027100	19.2093727
320	.0031250	17.8885438	370	.0027027	19.2353841
321	.0031153	17.9164729	371	.0026954	19.2613603
322	.0031056	17.9443584	372	.0026882	19.2873015
323	.0030960	17.9722008	373	.0026810	19.3132079
324	.0030864	18.0000000	374	.0026738	19.3390796
325	.0030769	18.0277564	375	.0026667	19.3649167
326	.0030675	18.0554701	376	.0026596	19.3907194
327	.0030581	18.0831413	377	.0026525	19.4164878
328	.0030488	18.1107703	378	.0026455	19.4422221
329	.0030395	18.1383571	379	.0026385	19.4679223
330	.0030303	18.1659021	380	.0026316	19.4935887
331	.0030211	18.1934054	381	.0026247	19.5192213
332	.0030120	18.2208672	382	.0026178	19.5448203
333	.0030030	18.2482876	383	.0026110	19.5703858
334	.0029940	18.2756669	384	.0026042	19.5959179
335	.0029851	18.3030052	385	.0025974	19.6214169
336	.0029762	18.3303028	386	.0025907	19.6468827
337	.0029674	18.3575598	387	.0025840	19.6723156
338	.0029586	18.3847763	388	.0025773	19.6977156
339	.0029499	18.4119526	389	.0025707	19.7230829
340	.0029412	18.4390889	390	.0025641	19.7484177
341	.0029326	18.4661853	391	.0025575	19.7737199
342	.0029240	18.4932420	392	.0025510	19.7989899
343	.0029155	18.5202592	393	.0025445	19.8242276
344	.0029070	18.5472370	394	.0025381	19.8494332
345	.0028986	18.5741756	395	.0025316	19.8746069
346	.0028902	18.6010752	396	.0025253	19.8997487
347	.0028818	18.6279360	397	.0025189	19.9248588
348	.0028736	18.6547581	398	.0025126	19.9499373
349	.0028653	18.6815417	399	.0025063	19.9749844
350	.0028571	18.7082869	400	.0025000	20.0000000

n	$\frac{1}{n}$	$\sqrt{n}$	n	$\frac{1}{n}$	$\sqrt{n}$
401	.0024938	20.0249844	451	.0022173	21.2367606
402	.0024876	20.0499377	452	.0022124	21.2602916
403	.0024814	20.0748599	453	.0022075	21.2837967
404	.0024752	20.0997512	454	.0022026	21.3072758
405	.0024691	20.1246118	455	.0021978	21.3307290
406	.0024631	20.1494417	456	.0021930	21.3541565
407	.0024570	20.1742410	457	.0021882	21.3775583
408	.0024510	20.1990099	458	.0021834	21.4009346
409	.0024450	20.2237484	459	.0021786	21.4242853
410	.0024390	20.2484567	460	.0021739	21.4476106
411	.0024331	20.2731349	461	.0021692	21.4709106
412	.0024272	20.2977831	462	.0021645	21.4941853
413	.0024213	20.3224014	463	.0021598	21.5174348
414	.0024155	20.3469899	464	.0021552	21.5406592
415	.0024096	20.3715488	465	.0021505	21.5638587
416	.0024038	20.3960781	466	.0021459	21.5870331
417	.0023981	20.4205779	467	.0021413	21.6101828
418	.0023923	20.4450483	468	.0021368	21.6333077
419	.0023866	20.4694895	469	.0021322	21.6564078
420	.0023810	20.4939015	470	.0021277	21.6794834
421	.0023753	20.5182845	471	.0021231	21.7025344
422	.0023697	20.5426386	472	.0021186	21.7255610
423	.0023641	20.5669638	473	.0021142	21.7485632
424	.0023585	20.5912603	474	.0021097	21.7715411
425	.0023529	20.6155281	475	.0021053	21.7944947
426	.0023474	20.6397674	476	.0021008	21.8174242
427	.0023419	20.6639783	477	.0020964	21.8403297
428	.0023364	20.6881609	478	.0020921	21.8632111
429	.0023310	20.7123152	479	.0020877	21.8860686
430	.0023256	20.7364414	480	.0020833	21.9089023
431	.0023202	20.7605395	481	.0020790	21.9317122
432	.0023148	20.7846097	482	.0020747	21.9544984
433	.0023095	20.8086520	483	.0020704	21.9772610
434	.0023041	20.8326667	484	.0020661	22.0000000
435	.0022989	20.8566536	485	.0020619	22.0227155
436	.0022936	20.8806130	486	.0020576	22.0454077
437	.0022883	20.9045450	487	.0020534	22.0680765
438	.0022831	20.9284495	488	.0020492	22.0907220
439	.0022779	20.9523268	489	.0020450	22.1133444
440	.0022727	20.9761770	490	.0020408	22.1359436
441	.0022676	21.0000000	491	.0020367	22.1585198
442	.0022624	21.0237960	492	.0020325	22.1810730
443	.0022573	21.0475652	493	.0020284	22.2036033
444	.0022523	21.0713075	494	.0020243	22.2261108
445	.0022472	21.0950231	495	.0020202	22.2485955
446	.0022422	21.1187121	496	.0020161	22.2710575
447	.0022371	21.1423745	497	.0020121	22.2934968
448	.0022321	21.1660105	498	.0020080	22.3159136
449	.0022272	21.1896201	499	.0020040	22.3383079
450	.0022222	21.2132034	500	.0020000	22.3606798

n	$\frac{1}{n}$	$\sqrt{n}$	n	$\frac{1}{n}$	$\sqrt{n}$
501	.0019960	22.3830293	551	.0018149	23.4733892
502	.0019920	22.4053565	552	.0018116	23.4946802
503	.0019881	22.4276615	553	.0018083	23.5159520
504	.0019841	22.4499443	554	.0018051	23.5372046
505	.0019802	22.4722051	555	.0018018	23.5584380
506	.0019763	22.4944438	556	.0017986	23.5796522
507	.0019724	22.5166605	557	.0017953	23.6008474
508	.0019685	22.5388553	558	.0017921	23.6220236
509	.0019646	22.5610283	559	.0017889	23.6431808
510	.0019608	22.5831796	560	.0017857	23.6643191
511	.0019569	22.6053091	561	.0017825	23.6854386
512	.0019531	22.6274170	562	.0017794	23.7065392
513	.0019493	22.6495033	563	.0017762	23.7276210
514	.0019455	22.6715681	564	.0017730	23.7486842
515	.0019417	22.6936114	565	.0017699	23.7697286
516	.0019380	22.7156334	566	.0017668	23.7907545
517	.0019342	22.7376340	567	.0017637	23.8117618
518	.0019305	22.7596134	568	.0017606	23.8327506
519	.0019268	22.7815715	569	.0017575	23.8537209
520	.0019231	22.8035085	570	.0017544	23.8746728
521	.0019194	22.8254244	571	.0017513	23.8956063
522	.0019157	22.8473193	572	.0017483	23.9165215
523	.0019120	22.8691933	573	.0017452	23.9374184
524	.0019084	22.8910463	574	.0017422	23.9582971
525	.0019048	22.9128785	575	.0017391	23.9791576
526	.0019011	22.9346899	576	.0017361	24.0000000
527	.0018975	22.9564806	577	.0017331	24.0208243
528	.0018939	22.9782506	578	.0017301	24.0416306
529	.0018904	23.0000000	579	.0017271	24.0624188
530	.0018868	23.0217289	580	.0017241	24.0831892
531	.0018832	23.0434372	581	.0017212	24.1039416
532	.0018797	23.0651252	582	.0017182	24.1246762
533	.0018762	23.0867928	583	.0017153	24.1453929
534	.0018727	23.1084400	584	.0017123	24.1660919
535	.0018692	23.1300670	585	.0017094	24.1867732
536	.0018657	23.1516738	586	.0017065	24.2074369
537	.0018622	23.1732605	587	.0017036	24.2280829
538	.0018587	23.1948270	588	.0017007	24.2487113
539	.0018553	23.2163735	589	.0016978	24.2693222
540	.0018519	23.2379001	590	.0016949	24.2899156
541	.0018484	23.2594067	591	.0016920	24.3104916
542	.0018450	23.2808935	592	.0016892	24.3310501
543	.0018416	23.3023604	593	.0016863	24.3515913
544	.0018382	23.3238076	594	.0016835	24.3721152
545	.0018349	23.3452351	595	.0016807	24.3926218
546	.0018315	23.3666429	596	.0016779	24.4131112
547	.0018282	23.3880311	597	.0016750	24.4335834
548	.0018248	23.4093998	598	.0016722	24.4540385
549	.0018215	23.4307490	599	.0016694	24.4744765
550	.0018182	23.4520788	600	.0016667	24.4948974

n	$\frac{1}{n}$	$\sqrt{n}$	n	$\frac{1}{n}$	$\sqrt{n}$
601	.0016639	24.5153013	651	.0015361	25.5147016
602	.0016611	24.5356883	652	.0015337	25.5342907
603	.0016584	24.5560583	653	.0015314	25.5538647
604	.0016556	24.5764115	654	.0015291	25.5734237
605	.0016529	24.5967478	655	.0015267	25.5929678
606	.0016502	24.6170673	656	.0015244	25.6124969
607	.0016474	24.6373700	657	.0015221	25.6320112
608	.0016447	24.6576560	658	.0015198	25.6515107
609	.0016420	24.6779254	659	.0015175	25.6709953
610	.0016393	24.6981781	660	.0015152	25.6904652
611	.0016367	24.7184142	661	.0015129	25.7099203
612	.0016340	24.7386338	662	.0015106	25.7293607
613	.0016313	24.7588368	663	.0015083	25.7487864
614	.0016287	24.7790234	664	.0015060	25.7681975
615	.0016260	24.7991935	665	.0015038	25.7875939
616	.0016234	24.8193473	666	.0015015	25.8069758
617	.0016207	24.8394847	667	.0014993	25.8263431
618	.0016181	24.8596058	668	.0014970	25.8456960
619	.0016155	24.8797106	669	.0014948	25.8650343
620	.0016129	24.8997992	670	.0014925	25.8843582
621	.0016103	24.9198716	671	.0014903	25.9036677
622	.0016077	24.9399278	672	.0014881	25.9229628
623	.0016051	24.9599679	673	.0014859	25.9422435
624	.0016026	24.9799920	674	.0014837	25.9615100
625	.0016000	25.0000000	675	.0014815	25.9807621
626	.0015974	25.0199920	676	.0014793	26.0000000
627	.0015949	25.0399681	677	.0014771	26.0192237
628	.0015924	25.0599282	678	.0014749	26.0384331
629	.0015898	25.0798724	679	.0014728	26.0576284
630	.0015873	25.0998008	680	.0014706	26.0768096
631	.0015848	25.1197134	681	.0014684	26.0959767
632	.0015823	25.1396102	682	.0014663	26.1151297
633	.0015798	25.1594913	683	.0014641	26.1342687
634	.0015773	25.1793566	684	.0014620	26.1533937
635	.0015748	25.1992063	685	.0014599	26.1725047
636	.0015723	25.2190404	686	.0014577	26.1916017
637	.0015699	25.2388589	687	.0014556	26.2106848
638	.0015674	25.2586619	688	.0014535	26.2297541
639	.0015649	25.2784493	689	.0014514	26.2488095
640	.0015625	25.2982213	690	.0014493	26.2678511
641	.0015601	25.3179778	691	.0014472	26.2868789
642	.0015576	25.3377189	692	.0014451	26.3058929
643	.0015552	25.3574447	693	.0014430	26.3248932
644	.0015528	25.3771551	694	.0014409	26.3438797
645	.0015504	25.3968502	695	.0014388	26.3628527
646	.0015480	25.4165301	696	.0014368	26.3818119
647	.0015456	25.4361947	697	.0014347	26.4007576
648	.0015432	25.4558441	698	.0014327	26.4196896
649	.0015408	25.4754784	699	.0014306	26.4386081
650	.0015385	25.4950976	700	.0014286	26.4575131

n	$\frac{1}{n}$	$\sqrt{n}$	n	$\frac{1}{n}$	$\sqrt{n}$
701	.0014265	26.4764046	751	.0013316	27.4043792
702	.0014245	26.4952825	752	.0013298	27.4226184
703	.0014225	26.5141472	753	.0013280	27.4408455
704	.0014205	26.5329983	754	.0013263	27.4590604
705	.0014184	26.5518361	755	.0013245	27.4772633
706	.0014164	26.5706605	756	.0013228	27.4954542
707	.0014144	26.5894716	757	.0013210	27.5136330
708	.0014124	26.6082694	758	.0013193	27.5317998
709	.0014104	26.6270539	759	.0013175	27.5499546
710	.0014085	26.6458252	760	.0013158	27.5680975
711	.0014065	26.6645833	761	.0013141	27.5862284
712	.0014045	26.6833281	762	.0013123	27.6043475
713	.0014025	26.7020598	763	.0013106	27.6224546
714	.0014006	26.7207784	764	.0013089	27.6405499
715	.0013986	26.7394839	765	.0013072	27.6586334
716	.0013966	26.7581763	766	.0013055	27.6767050
717	.0013947	26.7768557	767	.0013038	27.6947648
718	.0013928	26.7955220	768	.0013021	27.7128129
719	.0013908	26.8141754	769	.0013004	27.7308492
720	.0013889	26.8328157	770	.0012987	27.7488739
721	.0013870	26.8514432	771	.0012970	27.7668868
722	.0013850	26.8700577	772	.0012953	27.7848880
723	.0013831	26.8886593	773	.0012937	27.8028775
724	.0013812	26.9072481	774	.0012920	27.8208555
725	.0013793	26.9258240	775	.0012903	27.8388218
726	.0013774	26.9443872	776	.0012887	27.8567766
727	.0013755	26.9629375	777	.0012870	27.8747197
728	.0013736	26.9814751	778	.0012853	27.8926514
729	.0013717	27.0000000	779	.0012837	27.9105715
730	.0013699	27.0185122	780	.0012821	27.9284801
731	.0013680	27.0370117	781	.0012804	27.9463772
732	.0013661	27.0554985	782	.0012788	27.9642629
733	.0013643	27.0739727	783	.0012771	27.9821372
734	.0013624	27.0924344	784	.0012755	28.0000000
735	.0013605	27.1108834	785	.0012739	28.0178515
736	.0013587	27.1293199	786	.0012723	28.0356915
737	.0013569	27.1477439	787	.0012706	28.0535203
738	.0013550	27.1661554	788	.0012690	28.0713377
739	.0013532	27.1845544	789	.0012674	28.0891438
740	.0013514	27.2029410	790	.0012658	28.1069386
741	.0013495	27.2213152	791	.0012642	28.1247222
742	.0013477	27.2396769	792	.0012626	28.1424946
743	.0013459	27.2580263	793	.0012610	28.1602557
744	.0013441	27.2763634	794	.0012594	28.1780056
745	.0013423	27.2946881	795	.0012579	28.1957444
746	.0013405	27.3130006	796	.0012563	28.2134720
747	.0013387	27.3313007	797	.0012547	28.2311884
748	.0013369	27.3495887	798	.0012531	28.2488938
749	.0013351	27.3678644	799	.0012516	28.2665881
750	.0013333	27.3861279	800	.0012500	28.2842712

n	$\frac{1}{n}$	$\sqrt{n}$	n	$\frac{1}{n}$	$\sqrt{n}$
801	,0012484	28,3019434	851	,0011751	29,1719043
802	,0012469	28,3196045	852	,0011737	29,1890390
803	,0012453	28,3372546	853	,0011723	29,2061637
804	,0012438	28,3548938	854	,0011710	29,2232784
805	,0012422	28,3725219	855	,0011696	29,2403830
806	,0012407	28,3901391	856	,0011682	29,2574777
807	,0012392	28,4077454	857	,0011669	29,2745623
808	,0012376	28,4253408	858	,0011655	29,2916370
809	,0012361	28,4429253	859	,0011641	29,3087018
810	,0012346	28,4604989	860	,0011628	29,3257566
811	,0012330	28,4780617	861	,0011614	29,3428015
812	,0012315	28,4956137	862	,0011601	29,3598365
813	,0012300	28,5131549	863	,0011587	29,3768616
814	,0012285	28,5306852	864	,0011574	29,3938769
815	,0012270	28,5482048	865	,0011561	29,4108823
816	,0012255	28,5657137	866	,0011547	29,4278779
817	,0012240	28,5832119	867	,0011534	29,4448637
818	,0012225	28,6006993	868	,0011521	29,4618397
819	,0012210	28,6181760	869	,0011507	29,4788059
820	,0012195	28,6356421	870	,0011494	29,4957624
821	,0012180	28,6530976	871	,0011481	29,5127091
822	,0012165	28,6705424	872	,0011468	29,5296461
823	,0012151	28,6879766	873	,0011455	29,5465734
824	,0012136	28,7054002	874	,0011442	29,5634910
825	,0012121	28,7228132	875	,0011429	29,5803989
826	,0012107	28,7402157	876	,0011416	29,5972972
827	,0012092	28,7576077	877	,0011403	29,6141858
828	,0012077	28,7749891	878	,0011390	29,6310648
829	,0012063	28,7923601	879	,0011377	29,6479342
830	,0012048	28,8097206	880	,0011364	29,6647939
831	,0012034	28,8270706	881	,0011351	29,6816442
832	,0012019	28,8444102	882	,0011338	29,6984848
833	,0012005	28,8617394	883	,0011325	29,7153159
834	,0011990	28,8790582	884	,0011312	29,7321375
835	,0011976	28,8963666	885	,0011299	29,7489496
836	,0011962	28,9136646	886	,0011287	29,7657521
837	,0011947	28,9309523	887	,0011274	29,7825452
838	,0011933	28,9482297	888	,0011261	29,7993289
839	,0011919	28,9654967	889	,0011249	29,8161030
840	,0011905	28,9827535	890	,0011236	29,8328678
841	,0011891	29,0000000	891	,0011223	29,8496231
842	,0011876	29,0172363	892	,0011211	29,8663690
843	,0011862	29,0344623	893	,0011198	29,8831056
844	,0011848	29,0516781	894	,0011186	29,8998328
845	,0011834	29,0688837	895	,0011173	29,9165506
846	,0011820	29,0860791	896	,0011161	29,9332591
847	,0011806	29,1032644	897	,0011148	29,9499583
848	,0011792	29,1204396	898	,0011136	29,9666481
849	,0011779	29,1376046	899	,0011123	29,9833287
850	,0011765	29,1547595	900	,0011111	30,0000000

n	1/n	√n	n	1/n	√n
901	.0011099	30.0166620	951	.0010515	30.8382879
902	.0011086	30.0333148	952	.0010504	30.8544972
903	.0011074	30.0499584	953	.0010493	30.8706981
904	.0011062	30.0665928	954	.0010482	30.8868904
905	.0011050	30.0832179	955	.0010471	30.9030743
906	.0011038	30.0998339	956	.0010460	30.9192497
907	.0011025	30.1164407	957	.0010449	30.9354166
908	.0011013	30.1330383	958	.0010438	30.9515751
909	.0011001	30.1496269	959	.0010428	30.9677251
910	.0010989	30.1662063	960	.0010417	30.9838668
911	.0010977	30.1827765	961	.0010406	31.0000000
912	.0010965	30.1993377	962	.0010395	31.0161248
913	.0010953	30.2158899	963	.0010384	31.0322413
914	.0010941	30.2324329	964	.0010373	31.0483494
915	.0010929	30.2489669	965	.0010363	31.0644491
916	.0010917	30.2654919	966	.0010352	31.0805405
917	.0010905	30.2820079	967	.0010341	31.0966236
918	.0010893	30.2985148	968	.0010331	31.1126984
919	.0010881	30.3150128	969	.0010320	31.1287648
920	.0010870	30.3315018	970	.0010309	31.1448230
921	.0010858	30.3479818	971	.0010299	31.1608729
922	.0010846	30.3644529	972	.0010288	31.1769145
923	.0010834	30.3809151	973	.0010277	31.1929479
924	.0010823	30.3973683	974	.0010267	31.2089731
925	.0010811	30.4138127	975	.0010256	31.2249900
926	.0010799	30.4302481	976	.0010246	31.2409987
927	.0010787	30.4466747	977	.0010235	31.2569992
928	.0010776	30.4630924	978	.0010225	31.2729915
929	.0010764	30.4795013	979	.0010215	31.2889757
930	.0010753	30.4959014	980	.0010204	31.3049517
931	.0010741	30.5122926	981	.0010194	31.3209195
932	.0010730	30.5286750	982	.0010183	31.3368792
933	.0010718	30.5450487	983	.0010173	31.3528308
934	.0010707	30.5614136	984	.0010163	31.3687743
935	.0010695	30.5777697	985	.0010152	31.3847097
936	.0010684	30.5941171	986	.0010142	31.4006369
937	.0010672	30.6104557	987	.0010132	31.4165561
938	.0010661	30.6267857	988	.0010121	31.4324673
939	.0010650	30.6431069	989	.0010111	31.4483704
940	.0010638	30.6594194	990	.0010101	31.4642654
941	.0010627	30.6757233	991	.0010091	31.4801525
942	.0010616	30.6920185	992	.0010081	31.4960315
943	.0010604	30.7083051	993	.0010070	31.5119025
944	.0010593	30.7245830	994	.0010060	31.5277655
945	.0010582	30.7408523	995	.0010050	31.5436206
946	.0010571	30.7571130	996	.0010040	31.5594677
947	.0010560	30.7733651	997	.0010030	31.5753068
948	.0010549	30.7896086	998	.0010020	31.5911380
949	.0010537	30.8058436	999	.0010010	31.6069613
950	.0010526	30.8220700	1000	.0010000	31.6227766

APPENDIX E

ANSWERS TO SAMPLE PROBLEMS

CHAPTER 2

(1) 638. or 638
(2) 47.227
(3) 1574. or 1574
(4) 5.8
(5) 817. or 817
(6) 6.88152
(7) 7.5714285
(8) 1.3812544
(9) 25.066666
(10) – 4.38
(11 a) 3407.4
(b) 6701.22
(c) .0631
(d) – 2688.06
(e) 77900.736
(12 a) 43.902439
(b) 86.341463
(c) .000813
(d) – 34.634146
(e) 1003.7073
(13 a) 4
(b) 243
(c) 2401
(d) 7776
(e) 362.46709

(14) new guess = $\frac{1}{2}\left(\frac{\text{number}}{\text{guess}} + \text{guess}\right)$

(a) initial guess of 6
first approximation = 5.9166665
second approximation = 5.9160795
third approximation = 5.9160795

(b) initial guess of 7
first approximation = 7.0714285
second approximation = 7.0710675
third approximation = 7.0710675

(c) initial guess of 10
first approximation = 11
second approximation = 10.954545
third approximation = 10.954451
fourth approximation = 10.954451

(d) initial guess of 30
first approximation = 35.566666
second approximation = 35.131037
third approximation = 35.128336
fourth approximation = 35.128336

CHAPTER 4

Expense Sheet

Rent—9.40% decrease in 1973
Miscellaneous—32.97% increase in 1973

Inventory

Buttons	54.50
Fabric A	1,575.00
Fabric B	3,000.00
Fabric C	103.75
Cotton	200.00
Needles	45.00
Soap	18.00
	$ 4,996.25

Grand Total of Sums

(1) $175.55
(2) $198.09
(3) $113.72
Grand total = $487.36

Hourly Payroll

Gross pay = $205.64
Net pay = $118.14

Overtime Payroll

Gross pay

(1) $(1.5 \times 7 + 35) \times 3.80 = 172.90$
Subtracting the deductions yields net pay of $128.44

(2) Gross pay = $222.60
Net pay = 146.97

Piecework Payroll

14 × $1.80 =	$25.20
35 × $1.15	40.25
16 × $1.25	20.00
43 × $1.10	47.30
Gross pay	$132.75

Commissions

$850.00 @ 13% ≐	$110.50
$642.00 @ 16% =	$102.72
$500.00 @ 11% =	$ 55.00
$480.00 @ 14% =	$ 67.20
Gross pay =	$335.42

Straight-Line Depreciation

Age	Periodic Depreciation	Depreciated Value	Total Accumulated Depreciation
0	—	10,462.	0.
1	830.	9,632.	830.
2	830.	8,802.	1,660.
3	830.	7,972.	2,490.
4	830.	7,142.	3,320.
5	830.	6,312.	4,150.
6	830.	5,482.	4,980.
7	830.	4,652.	5,810.
8	830.	3,822.	6,640.
9	830.	2,992.	7,470.
10	830.	2,162.	8,300.
11	830.	1,332.	9,130.
12	830.	502.	9,960.

Sales Profit and Loss

(1) Cost of loaves 1020 × .12 = $122.40
+ shipping 85.00

Total cost to baker = $207.40
Return = 1020 × .20 = 204.00

Baker's loss = $3.40
Percentage Loss = 1.6%

(2) 405 @ $3.25 = $1316.25
360 @ $3.35 = 1206.00
310 @ $3.43 = 1063.30

$3585.55

Cost to factory =

$$(405 + 360 + 310) \times \$1.05 = \$1128.75$$

plus trucking = 53.10

Total cost $1181.85

$$\begin{array}{r} \$3585.55 \\ -\ 1181.85 \\ \hline \end{array}$$

Net gain = $2403.70

CHAPTER 6

Interest on Money

(1) Formula to use is $i = prt$
where

$$p = \$1{,}850$$

$$r = 6\tfrac{3}{4}\,\% = .0675$$

$$t = \frac{95}{360} \text{ years}$$

Answer is $32.95

(2) Use the same formula as (1), but for the exact interest divide by 365 instead of 360.

Simple interest = $31.25
Exact simple interest = $30.82

(3) In this problem, we have to do some thinking before we can calculate. Let x be the amount to be invested for 6 months at 5%.

$$i = prt$$

or

$$i = x(.05)(.5)$$

$$= .025x$$

$$.025x + x = \$2050.00$$

$$1.025x = 2050$$

$$x = \frac{2050}{1.025} = 2{,}000$$

The original amount invested was therefore $2,000.

(4) $t = \frac{i}{pr}$

$$t = \frac{6}{900(.0525)} \times 360 = 46 \text{ days}$$

Compound Interest

(1) $S = P(1 + i)^n$

where $P = \$8{,}300$

i = the interest rate per compound period

$= \frac{.0625}{4}$

$= .015625$

$n = 2 \text{ years} \times 4 \text{ periods per year} = 8$

$S = (8{,}300)(1 + .015625)^8 = \$9{,}396.04$

(2) $S = P(1 + i)^n$

where $P = \$1{,}000$

$i = \frac{.054}{2} = .027$

$n = 2 \times 3 = 6$

$S = 1{,}000\,(1 + .027)^6 = \$1{,}173.34$

Perpetuities

(1) $A = \frac{R}{i}$

where $R = \$850$

$i = .04$

$A = \frac{850}{.04} = \$21{,}250$

(2) $i = \frac{R}{A}$

$i = \frac{10{,}000}{68{,}000} = .1470588235$

$= 14.7\%$

(3) $R = Ai$

$= (50{,}000)(.08)$

$= \$4{,}000$

CHAPTER 7

Reciprocals

(1) In one minute,

Worker A can dig $\frac{1}{45}$ of the trench

Worker B can dig $\frac{1}{30}$ of the trench

Worker C can dig $\frac{1}{52}$ of the trench.

Therefore in one minute, working together, they can dig:

$$\frac{1}{45} + \frac{1}{30} + \frac{1}{52} \text{ of the trench}$$

$$= .0222222 + .0333333 + .0192307$$

$$= .0747862$$

$$\frac{1}{.0747862} = 13.3715 \text{ minutes}$$

(2)

$$= \frac{1}{R_{total}} = \frac{1}{R_1} + \frac{1}{R_2} + \frac{1}{R_3} + \frac{1}{R_4}$$

$$= \frac{1}{21} + \frac{1}{24} + \frac{1}{30} + \frac{1}{36}$$

$$= .047619 + .0416666 + .0333333 + .0277777$$

$$= .1503966$$

$$R_{total} = \frac{1}{.1503966} = 6.6490864$$

Temperature Conversion

Centigrade to Fahrenheit

(1) 107.6°F
(2) 149°F
(3) –40°F
(4) 32°F

Fahrenheit to Centigrade

(1) 8.89°C
(2) 15.62°C
(3) –40°C
(4) –17.78°C